2004 POETRY

ONCE UPON A RHYME

IMAGINATION FOR A NEW GENERATION

C000050108

Gloucestershire

Edited by Steve Twelvetree

August 2004

Dear Aunty Sue & Uncle Nigel,

You will find my poem on page 114. Enjoy!

Love from
Rosie
x x x x

 Young**Writers**

First published in Great Britain in 2004 by:
Young Writers
Remus House
Coltsfoot Drive
Peterborough
PE2 9JX
Telephone: 01733 890066
Website: www.youngwriters.co.uk

© Copyright Contributors 2004

SB ISBN 1 84460 463 2

Foreword

Young Writers was established in 1991 and has been passionately devoted to the promotion of reading and writing in children and young adults ever since. The quest continues today. Young Writers remains as committed to engendering the fostering of burgeoning poetic and literary talent as ever.

This year's Young Writers competition has proven as vibrant and dynamic as ever and we are delighted to present a showcase of the best poetry from across the UK. Each poem has been carefully selected from a wealth of *Once Upon A Rhyme* entries before ultimately being published in this, our twelfth primary school poetry series.

Once again, we have been supremely impressed by the overall high quality of the entries we have received. The imagination, energy and creativity which has gone into each young writer's entry made choosing the best poems a challenging and often difficult but ultimately hugely rewarding task - the general high standard of the work submitted amply vindicating this opportunity to bring their poetry to a larger appreciative audience.

We sincerely hope you are pleased with our final selection and that you will enjoy *Once Upon A Rhyme Gloucestershire* for many years to come.

Contents

Bradley Hazard (10)   1

Bledington Primary School
Nicholas Mark Hyatt (11)   2
Benjamin James Pearson (10)   2
Lucy Jennings (9)   3
Harry King (11)   3
Jodie Tyack (10)   4
Ashley Hyatt (11)   4
Alexandra Elmer-Menage (11)   5
Eira Walling (10)   5
Bill Pearson (10)   6
Macinni Ella Meyer (9)   6
Toni Wilton (8)   6
Logan Bell (9)   7
Edina Chloe Imogen Morris (8)   7

Calton Junior School
Morgan Hunt (8)   8
Philip Shaw (10)   8
Chloe Sanders (10)   9
Curtis Neal (10)   9
Alixandra East (10)   10
Satya Talwar Mouland (10)   10
Laura Henderson (11)   11
Lucy Beard (10)   11

Charlton Kings Junior School
Angus Beveridge (10)   12
Tabitha Gibson (10)   12
Ross Corder (8)   12
George Carrie (8)   13
Vicky Bee (11)   13
Jessica Winnan (11)   14

Churchdown Village Junior School

Alice Evans (9)	14
Sam Fizor (9)	15
Zoe Thomson (10)	15
Jacob Fox (9)	16
Melissa Davenport (8)	16
Olivia Yates (9)	17
Jennifer Smee (8)	17
Laura Guest (8)	18
Bradley Tonks (8)	18
Jessica Smith (8)	19
Laura Jones (8)	19
Bill Clark (10)	20
Hannah Carter (11)	20
Beth Curtis (10)	21
Hannah Gibson (10)	22
Bethany Joy (10)	22
Christine Badger (11)	23
Katie Fryatt (8)	23
Leonie Hammond (10)	24
Nicola Vizard (9)	24
Emma Nield (8)	25
Tom Batchelor (8)	25
Victoria Weare (9)	26
April Salcombe (8)	26
Edmund Rhys Jones (7)	27

Dursley Primary School

Sam Broder (11)	27
Katy Greenhill (10)	27
Harriet Coates (11)	28
Nathan Pretty (10)	28
Alice Wright (11)	29
Jake Woods (11)	29
Hollie Ind-Smith (11)	30
Jennifer Wong (10)	30
Jamie Griffey (10)	31
Aaron Darlow (10)	31
Benjamin Lewis (10)	32
Ella Hitchcox (10)	32
Simon Thomas (10)	33

Lara Lovegrove (11) 33
Emily Lyons (10) 34
Jake Cooke 34
Kirsty Reynolds (11) 35
Robert Bartlett 35
Rebecca Carrier (10) 36
Rebecca Crane (10) 36
Jake Williams (11) 36
Kenny Smith (11) 37
Katherine Hamilton 38

Field Court Junior School

Aaron Powick (9) 38
Samuel Digby (9) 39
Liam Wallwork-Gush (10) 39
Holly Carrick (10) 40
Aaron Meredith (10) 40
Connar Westgate (10) 40
Joshua Etherton (9) 41
Gemma King (10) 41
Callum Marshall (9) 41
Rebecca Burrows (9) 42
Kimberley Brooks (10) 42
Zoe Bartholomew (9) 43
Shannon Newcombe (10) 43
Summer Hynam (9) 44
Kayleigh Hather (10) 44
Ryan Greenwood (10) 44
Zoë Jenner (10) 45
Gregory Gibbs (9) 45
Lauren Ferris (8) 45
Kayleigh Fryer (8) 46
Jake Butt (10) 46
Abigail Humphris (9) 47
Charlie Gardiner (9) 47
Georgia Crisp (8) 48
Josh Bingham (8) 48
Sean Jarrett (9) 49
Joshua Hayward (8) 49
Lauren Alps (8) 50
Phoebe Embling (8) 50

Dawn Barlow (9)   51
Daniel Westgate (8)   52
Scott Oram (8)   52
Chloe Buckley (8)   53
Hannah Orchard (8)   53
Michael Poat (9)   54
Charlotte Emery (9)   54
Serena Deakins (8)   55
Dean Pearce (9)   55
Jason Burt (9)   56
Ryan Butt (10)   56
Sophie Barton (8)   56

Hillview CP School
Emily Stevens (11)   57
Rebecca Wyse (10)   57
H Crosby   58
Sean West   58
Anwen Carter (11)   59
James Russell (10)   59
Alice Watkins (11)   60
Tashan Vadher   60
Daniel Hill (11)   61
Kayne Cook   61
Tracie Grieve (11)   62
Laura Faulkner (10)   63
Lucie Allen (11)   64
Krystal Ricketts   65
Samuel Wheeler (11)   66
George Batt (11)   67
Emily Prince & Hannah Dewick (11)   68
Liam Long (10)   69
Lauren Smith (11)   70
Megan Goode (10)   71
Matthew Davis (10)   72

Lakeside Primary School
Ethan Buxton (9)   72
Joanne Crisp (10)   73
Lucy Bartrick (11)   73
Kayleigh Tompkins (9)   74

Abigail Stacey (7)   74
Jessica Halsall (9)   75
Jonathan Morris (10)   75
Kate Dickinson (9)   76
Evie Page (8)   76
Roxana Shafiee (10)   77
Beverley Fricker (10)   77
Gaby Pugh (7)   78

Leckhampton Primary School
Martha Kelsey (8)   79
Toby Burden (8)   80
George Kimpton (9)   81
Sophie Goodrum (9)   82
Harry Corder-Gill (8)   83
Anna McNeir (8)   84
Katie Smith (8)   85
Catherine Hyde (8)   86
Charles Glover (8)   87
Alice Winter (8)   88
Charlotte Buchanan (9)   89
Christopher Hope (9)   90
Bradley Hearn (9)   91

Leonard Stanley Primary School
Rory Birch (11)   91
Jodie Atkins (11)   92
Calum Murdock (10)   92
Megan Roberts (11)   93
Luke Murdock (10)   93
Lauren Oakes (11)   94
Ellen O'Dowd (11)   94
Bethany Timbrell (10)   95
Megan Uzzell (9)   95
Alex Smith (10)   96
Oliver Harford (10)   96
Nicole Clements (9)   97
Lorna Poultney (10)   97
Leanne Harnden (10)   98
Danielle Cole (10)   98
Samuel Jones (9)   99

Scott Carrington	99
Sam Pinker (9)	100
Oliver Cooper (10)	100
Georgia Matthews (9)	100
Ella Harriss (10)	101
Ford Sass (8)	102
Prudence Morgan-Wood (9)	102
William Richardson (8)	102
Ben Sztanko (8)	102

Nailsworth CE Primary School

Mackenzie Young (9)	103
Jacob Chew (10)	103
Hannah Ravenhill (10)	104
Izzy Davis (10)	104
Henry Watts (9)	105
Rebecca Long (10)	105
Katie Gay (9)	106
Chloe Marsden (10)	106
Simon Amos (9)	106
Mustafijur Rohman (10)	107

Northleach CE Primary School

Gaby Chilton (10)	107
Kirstie Smith (11)	108
Bethany Collado (10)	108
Laura See (10)	109
Thomas Williams (10)	109
Hannah Creed (11)	110
Aiden Bassett (11)	110
Ashleigh Rudd (11)	111
Richard Tapsell (11)	111
Ellen Wilkins (10)	112
Chris Mills (10)	113
Rosie Leach (10)	114
Michael Kent (10)	114
Henry Fothergill (11)	115
Jo Drinkwater (10)	115

Parkend Primary School

Chloe Phillips (9)	116
George Stratford (7)	116
Claire Preest (9)	117
Laura Taylor (5)	117
Rhees Davis (11)	118
Craig Hinchliffe (6)	118
Lara Shingles (10)	119
Joe Thomas (6)	119
Thomas Hodder (11)	120
Liam Sheppard (7)	120
Hannah O'Connell (10)	121
Eleanor Brown (5)	121
Chelsea Turley (10)	122
Hollie Seaborn (6)	122
Stuart Jones (9)	123
Kerri Davis (10)	123
Jed Leach (11)	124
Jack Brace (10)	124
Matthew Powell (10)	125
Jake Fletcher (8)	125
Henry Jones (9)	126
Joseph Aldridge (9)	126
Rowan Uzzell (9)	127
Ross James (7)	127
Alex Brown (9)	128
Ella Warsop (8)	128
Matthew Aldridge (9)	128
Benjamin Stratford (9)	129
Stuart Clarke (7)	129
Emily Worgan (9)	129
Savanna Tyler (9)	130
Otto Linden (7)	130
Jack Turley (8)	131
Alasdair Hinchliffe (10)	131
Alex Hooper (8)	132
Faye Lewis (9)	132
Dan Pope (9)	132
Lauren Roberts (7)	133

St Anthony's Convent School, Cinderford

Jason Roberts (11)	133
Katherine MacLean (11)	134
Thomas Tremlett (10)	134
Daniel Bell (10)	135
Sophie Linton (10)	135
Ben Stephens (11)	136
James Hamell (10)	136
Callum Ireland (10)	137
Christina O'Carroll (11)	138
Chloe Walding (10)	139
Oliver Fitt (11)	140
Jessica Mason (10)	141
Karl Turner (11)	142
Holly Smith (10)	143

St David's Primary School, Moreton-in-Marsh

Gwennan Williams (8)	143
Catriona Wilcox (8)	144
Lucy Jasinski (11)	144
Daisy Lindlar (11)	145
Rhiannon Davies (10)	145
Rhiannon Williams (9)	146
Phoebe Jarvis (11)	146
Elliot Langley (9)	147
Kitty Mounstephen (11)	147
Sarah Thompson (9)	147

St Paul's CE Primary School, Gloucester

April Bailey (8)	148
Lucy Peck (9)	148
Bradley Meredith (8)	149
Conrad Jones (8)	149
Solima Ali (8)	149
Georgina Lefeuvre (9)	150
Scott Rickards (9)	150
Jonah Windo (9)	150
Elliot Etherton (8)	151
Sam Collins (9)	151
Luke Campbell (9)	151
Yahya Pandor (9)	152

Daniel Cratchley (8)   152
Keeland Anderson (9)   153

Siddington CE Primary School
Cameron Frerker (12)   153
Emily Kilby (10)   154
Emily Cordon (10)   154
Daniella Keen (9)   155
Scarlett Collins (10)   155
Charmaine Linton (10)   156
Luke Moore (11)   156
Aaron Saunders (11)   156
Charlotte Tickle (9)   157
Letisha Jessop (10)   157
Ryan Rogers (10)   157
Keegan Giles (10)   158

Temple Guiting School
Thomas Clare (8)   158
Rosalind Ball (8)   158
Dido Bolton (8)   159
Camilla Mather (9)   159
Max Holland (7)   159
Daniel Feaster (8)   160
Jemma Moore (9)   160
Daniel Moore (7)   160
William Twiston-Davies (9)   161
Suzannah Wiggins (8)   161
Laura Shelley (8)   161
Charli-Ann Porter (8)   162
Luke Tatlow (9)   162
Sophia Kelly (8)   162
Olivia Morrissey (7)   163
Sophie Andrews (7)   163
Joseph Stirling Lee (8)   163
Alice Wynn (8)   164
Rowland Bowen-Jones (8)   164
Christian Forbes (7)   164

Uplands CP School

Stephanie Beard (11)	165
Ottilie Baker (9)	165
Ruth Townley (10)	165
Elizabeth Locke (10)	166
Samantha Tozer (10)	166
Cameron Kyte (10)	167
Kelly Bartlett (11)	167
Ryan Thwaite (10)	168
McCoy Tinsey (10)	168
Roseanna Dressel (10)	169
Jamie Mather (11)	169
Hannah Cullis (10)	170
Liam Deane (10)	170
Thomas Legge (9)	170
Tim Parnell (9)	171
Peter Costello (11)	171
Daniel Omnes (10)	171
Daniel Button (10)	172
Holly Clay (10)	172
Jade Riches (9)	173
Bradley Gardiner	173

Woodmancote Primary School

Holly Hart (10)	173
Stephen Dolman (9)	174
Michael Robey (9)	174
Georgina Burrows (10)	175
Louisa Ripley (9)	175
Eleanor Walsh (9)	176
Emily Mackenzie (9)	176
Laura Winstanley (10)	176
Felix Torrance (9)	177
Jasmin Weaver (9)	177
Hannah Andrews (7)	177
Alexis Munro (10)	178
Evie Torrance (7)	179
Joshua Phillips (10)	180
Georgia Lines (6)	181
Emma Jenkins (7)	181
Philippa Rawlinson (7)	182

Ellie Knight (7) 182
Amy Finch (9) 183
Jessica Butler (7) 183

Wycliffe Preparatory School

Charlie Hitchcock (8) 184
Kerianne Genders (7) 184
Victoria Dickinson (7) 184
Kieran Powell (8) 185
Oliver Cawthorne (7) 185
Imogen Bell (7) 185
Charlotte Macpherson-Spence (8) 186
Fiona Kennedy (8) 186
Harry Hemming (7) 186
Saffron Teagle-Brown (7) 187
Lewis McKissick (8) 187
Patrick Price (8) 187
Fergus Menendez (8) 188
Lucy Moule (8) 188
Jemma Buck (7) 188
Rachel Connolly (8) 189
Jasmine Bailey (8) 189
Henry Scott (7) 189
Aimee Wilkinson (7) 190
Ralph Williams (8) 190
Benjamin Capehorn (7) 190
Ruth Vickers (8) 191
Camila Poccard (8) 191

The Poems

The Greatest Nightmare

I sat up straight in my bed,
I heard something or was it in my head?
There was a shadow on the wall,
And then the shadow began to fall.

Whoever he was I heard him speaking,
Then there was a massive creaking,
I was now in fright,
Worst of all in the night.

Out jumped a giant spider on my face,
Then I yelled please Lord grace,
But I believed in myself and said back
'I'm running away before I'm getting hacked'

So he bravely ran away, he bravely ran away
Once he saw a spider head
He turned around then he fled
He screamed and shouted and woke up in bed

Sitting there in his chair
Thinking with his scruffy hair
If what happened was really true
He could have been turned to spider poo

Then jumped out a little one
And bit him straight on his bum
He yelled, 'Ouch'
And fell on the couch

Then it crawled in his pants
So he did a little dance
He woke up the second time
Because that's my rhyme.

Bradley Hazard (10)

Nature Is Quiet

N ature is not man-made
A tree has a squirrel running up it,
T he dark green buds bloom into beautiful flowers.
U nder dark oak trees are delicate roots,
R ivers dangerously flowing into dangerous waterfalls,
E nding nature is not possible.

I n the cold wind, red crunchy leaves fall,
S quirrels eat and hide brown wrinkled nuts.

Q uietly, shiny purple beetles crawl along,
U nder the mushrooms, red and black ladybirds sleep.
I n the dark gloomy sky, moths fly quickly,
E very insect has a place -
T he nature in this world is the best.

Nicholas Mark Hyatt (11)
Bledington Primary School

If I Was . . .

If I was the moon I'd jump upon the stars,
If I was the moon I'd make friends with Mars.

If I was a swan I'd glide along the lake,
If I was a swan I'd never be late.

If I was the wind I'd conjure up a gale,
If I was the wind I'd send a roaring gale.

If I was a wave I'd crash and thrash and roar,
If I was a wave I'd race along the shore.

If I was an eagle I'd make my nest all day,
If I was an eagle I'd go and hunt my prey.

Benjamin James Pearson (10)
Bledington Primary School

Nature

I saw fluttering butterflies,
Scuttling beetles,
Spotty ladybirds
That's what I saw on my walk into ature.

I saw three little cute birds perched on branches
Terrifying black widow spiders.
Tiny baby deers
That's what I saw on my walk into nature.

I saw fluffy squirrels,
Extremely smelly skunks,
Slimy worms.
That's what I saw on my walk into nature.

I saw crunchy leaves,
Wild flowers of different colours,
A flowing river.
That's what I saw on my walk into nature.

I love nature.

Lucy Jennings (9)
Bledington Primary School

Grampy King

I wonder if my Gramp will come back,
My heart wonders into my dreams.
The hope that I would see him once more,
In a dream or in reality, maybe.

Life would be fabulous forever, if you knew him,
Wishes could work or perhaps not.
Life would not be extraordinary without wishing .
The grave is solid as can be, like a mountain going on forever.
The grass is comfy like warm crumpets.

Harry King (11)
Bledington Primary School

The Hole Which I Found

There was once a hole which I found,
It probably leads beneath the ground.
Walking in the wet, wet, wet.
Other people I met, met, met.
Really though, it's my special place,
They're just my servants in trace, trace, trace.
Then I get on my special, secret broom,
Up and down, zoom, zoom, zoom.
Laugh along,
Jump up high,
Wash them down.
Then you feel like you're going to die.
You have to walk in a savage case,
Scattered mud all over the place.
Squelch, squelch wherever you go,
Uh oh! I think the broom's gone mad
Take cover!
Oh no!
Here I am at my special place,
Someone's coming, I'd better race.

Jodie Tyack (10)
Bledington Primary School

The Sea

T is for the sand gleaming in the sun
H is for heads, coming out of the water, ready for a bun
E is for everyone as happy as can be.

S is for the sun, golden in the sky,
E is for electric eel at the end of a pier,
A is for animals in the sea.

Ashley Hyatt (11)
Bledington Primary School

My Special Place

My special place has sand like golden grains,
Sparkling in the sun,
Tickling your feet as you walk through it.

My special place has a sun as hot as a fire,
Shimmering down on the sea,
Shadows of surfers skimming across the sea.

My special place has people, babies screaming,
Children playing,
Teenagers sunbathing.

Do you know where I am?
I'm on holiday in Newquay.

Alexandra Elmer-Menage (11)
Bledington Primary School

Down By The Fairies

To the fairies down we go,
See the little river flow.
When I get angry or upset,
I go down and get wet.
See a flutter of a wing,
You might find a fairy king.

If you go to my special place,
You'll probably just trip over your lace.
I think it's time to say this now,
They don't know you -
So how you'll see them
I don't know how!

Eira Walling (10)
Bledington Primary School

Nature

The wood is full of life,
With red deer and grey squirrels,
Racing up tall trees.
Pretty bluebells,
Poking through the wet green grass.
Little streams trickling right through the big wood.
Massive boulders standing proud
Amongst crispy brown leaves.

Bill Pearson (10)
Bledington Primary School

Nature

N ature is such a wonderful part of life,
A nimals scurry around on the ground.
T ree branches swaying in the warm breeze,
U nicorns flying gently in the clear blue sky,
R obins looking for food in the cold winter,
E lephants having a wash with their trunks.

Macinni Ella Meyer (9)
Bledington Primary School

Nature

N ature is calm and peaceful,
A nimals scuttling around everywhere,
T rees swaying in the warm wind, rustling leaves,
U nicorns running and taking off into the sky,
R abbits hopping around happily in the warm sun,
E lephants stomping around very, very loudly.

Toni Wilton (8)
Bledington Primary School

The Forest Awakens

Rivers flowing rapidly,
like a swarm of squirrels trying to find nuts.

Hatching eggs,
like spun balls of golden string, slowly breaking.

Meadows of flowers,
following the sun wherever it moves.

Trees standing their ground,
like soldiers waiting for war.

And as the sun sets,
the forest falls asleep again.

Logan Bell (9)
Bledington Primary School

Animals

In the green hot jungle,
There are lots of animals,
Different shapes and sizes
Never-ending palm trees,
Standing in the hot sun.
Every day it changes,
The temperature
It gets hot and it gets colder.
When you get further on
You will find an extensive waterfall.
It's very dangerous when you walk around the sharp cliff -
After a while, it gets tiring.

Edina Chloe Imogen Morris (8)
Bledington Primary School

Foxes

Foxes have bushy tails
But don't deliver any mail.
They may be cute and fluffy
But you wouldn't like to meet one in a hurry.
Foxes are like a dog
But you shouldn't treat it like a frog.
There is such a thing as flying foxes,
You can't keep them in small boxes.
Foxes can bite
And they can give you a very big fright.
Arctic foxes are the best
But they don't live in a nest.
Foxes do have to eat
And they have very dog-like feet.
Foxes are very nice
But now and then they fancy some mice.
Foxes are brill, well to me they are
And as you know, they don't drive a car.
Foxes are very pretty
And sometimes take little pity.
Any colour and any shape,
You cannot have them as a big bait.

Morgan Hunt (8)
Calton Junior School

The Mysterious Forest

Trees guarding and protecting their territory,
An owl in the treetops, ready to eat prey,
Fairies flutter from their hiding place,
Wild unicorns galloping through trees,
The moonlight covers the forest like a carpet.

Philip Shaw (10)
Calton Junior School

My Twelve Songs

Stop the train from tracking
Leave the doorbells ringing
Prevent the world, a cheerful song
Silence those organs and hear the deep drums
Bring out the coffin, let them bow down to pray
Let my message be delivered
For my only loved one is dead
Let me share my feelings with the world, with presents and letters
Just once for me, let the white swans be grey

He was my east, my west, my north and south
My hard labour and my peace and rest
My day, my night and a note of every song
I thought his heart would not stop beating, I was wrong . . .

The beauty of the world is no longer wanted
For he is dead.

Chloe Sanders (10)
Calton Junior School

Hatred

Hatred,
It lurks there,
In the corner of the room,
Staring at you with animosity,
Waiting to clutch your brain,
Attacking with contempt,
Enmity sweeps across the floor,
You can smell the hostility.

Curtis Neal (10)
Calton Junior School

The One I Love

Stop the tigers roaring, calm the waves crashing
Prevent the taps from running
Silence the television blaring as the muffled drum is heard
Bring out the coffin, let us grieve
Let the banners fly in the sky giving the message he is dead
Put candles in every window
Let the loved ones raise from the dead.

He was my day, my week, my month and year
My hard work, my midnight rest
My spirit, my soul, my sadness, my joy
I thought our relationship would last forever, I was wrong.

Nature isn't needed now, chop down all the trees
Pack up the wildlife and burn them to ashes
Pour away the light blue sky
For nothing is worth living for, now my friend is dead.

Alixandra East (10)
Calton Junior School

Inspirational India

(Dedicated to my grandma)

India is an enchanting land of secrets and spice,
On the night of Diwali, candles flicker in the darkest night,
The sweet smell of incense perfumes the air,
People eat curries mixed with the finest spices,
Tourists visit the sacred temple Taj Mahal, made of cold white marble,
Elephants decorated in colourful paints take the children
Perching on their velvety rugs around the sandy beaches,
When someone has died, people dip in the holy river Ganges
                                   as a form of respect,
Images of Lord Krishna playing the flute brighten up people's lives,
I will remember the rhythmic tunes and bright colours of the
                                   wonderful land, India.

Satya Talwar Mouland (10)
Calton Junior School

Sea Life Wonder!

Under the sea
I wish I could be
A fish with a tail
A shark without fail
A jellyfish that would sting
A whale that sings
Oh! What could I be?

Under the sea
Oh! What would I be?
A crab that nips me
And octopuses I could see
Sea horses behind the seaweed
And sand at the bottom of the sea
Oh! What could I be?

Under the sea
Oh! I don't know what I could be
A swordfish that would follow me
A dolphin that is clean
So what could I be?
I think I'll just be me
Yes! I think I'll just be me.

Laura Henderson (11)
Calton Junior School

My Love

He is my love and will be, for his heart belongs to me
All the memories of our shared life will remain
As he passes the wetness of a tear rolls down my cheek
For I for one will revenge his death
If I'm the one I shall move to a new home
But not on Earth, in Heaven where all the angels go
If you turn against me, death will come upon you.

Lucy Beard (10)
Calton Junior School

War

War is a huge mistake
Bombs harm innocent civilians
Everyone suffers from wars, even the winners
Children imitate adults and fight
People should talk, not fight
Peace would make the world a better place to live
Aeroplanes should have better security
War ends when people agree.

Angus Beveridge (10)
Charlton Kings Junior School

War And Peace

War is sparring and full of woe
Peace is love and in our hearts
War is evil and full of woe
Peace is mature and full of respect
War is death and destroyed homes
Peace is living the right way
War is chemical gas filling the air
There is about ten wars a day, people die for selfish people.

Tabitha Gibson (10)
Charlton Kings Junior School

Staring Eyes

Creak . . . looking for arms . . . *creak*
To tickle unseen
Croak . . . corners, all cramped . . . *croak*
Up, peeping, balancing
Skitter . . . without moving on . . . *skitter*
The web waiting
Scatter . . . for flies to get . . . *scatter*
Trapped.

Ross Corder (8)
Charlton Kings Junior School

Eagle Beware!

My beak so fine
I break through the air
Fine and handsome
My wings divine
My feathers silky
My wings flapping slowly
My wingspan spreads in the freedom of the air
I hunt for rodents in the ground
I dip and dive
Swoop and glide
My wings shine in the sunlight
I am rare, so don't hunt me please
I am an eagle
The king of the sky.

George Carrie (8)
Charlton Kings Junior School

War And Peace

If the world was run by peace, it would be great,
There would be no more wars!
Peace is peaceful,
Peace means lucky faces,
Peace means delight,
War is cheerful for no people,
Stop killing people,
More and more equipment,
More and more guns
If we don't have war, children will be over the moon,
Stop invading other countries,
War means disappointed faces.

Vicky Bee (11)
Charlton Kings Junior School

War Or Peace

War is like a sprout, disgusting and no one appreciates it,
Peace is like a cupcake, lovely and everyone enjoys them!
In war you lose families and friends, instead of the world being friends,
Peace brings joy and delight to the world,
War leaves behind mess and sadness,
Peace brings together every nation,
War is destructive and normally unnecessary,
People just want land in war, which is greedy and selfish,
Lots of people die who are innocent and kind,
All wars are wrong and millions die each time,
If the world can't get on then they should stay away from each other,
Oh, why can't things just be settled over a cup of tea and biscuits?

Jessica Winnan (11)
Charlton Kings Junior School

Moons

The moon reflecting its light from the sun
Like a mirror on the moon
Its shape like a Viking ship sailing across the dark sheets of the sky

The crescent moon is like a friendly smile
On its side
As if it was staring at you

The changing moon is like a tilted 'C'
It is also like a half-bitten white chocolate
In a box of velvet night

The moon twirls and whirls like a ballerina
Dressed in white.

Alice Evans (9)
Churchdown Village Junior School

My Hamster

My hamster is called Snowflake
I feed him every day
He likes to chew on nuts
But not a bale of hay

Snowflake has white fur
Black splodges too
If he were much bigger
He'd be a panda in a zoo

Snowflake is quite noisy
When he's keeping fit
He spins his wheel round and round
Then jumps into his pit

After he's been training
He's awake throughout the night
Then he sleeps through the daytime
I'm sure this can't be right

So Snowflake is my hamster
He also is my friend
Even though I love him
He drives me round the bend.

Jacob Fox (9)
Churchdown Village Junior School

Noisy Town

Lorries stamp through the busy town
Babies scream, 'Where are my parents?'
Cars skid on the icy tarmac
With full trains zooming past
What a busy, noisy town
We're out of here!

Melissa Davenport (8)
Churchdown Village Junior School

Nowhere

It happened two years ago on the 7th January
And from then on it began.

On the night before my birthday
Where was he to be seen? Nowhere!

On the night before Christmas
Where was he to be seen? Nowhere!

On the night before New Year
Where was he to be seen? Nowhere!

On the night before Easter
Where was he to be seen? Nowhere!

And then a year later
On a not so cold morning, the phone rang.

I answered sleepily to hear the voice
I had for so long dreamed to hear

The voice of he who is nowhere

My dad!

Laura Guest (8)
Churchdown Village Junior School

My Grandmother

My grandmother was a wonderful thing
My grandmother could dance and sing
My grandmother would hold me very tight
My grandmother could tell me stories all night
My grandmother is now in Heaven
I like to pretend she's just popped to Devon!

Bradley Tonks (8)
Churchdown Village Junior School

The Moon

The silvery smiley face
Beaming upon
The Earth's silent grace

An enormous button
Sewn to
The black cloak of space

The Heaven's crescent arch
Raised in the night sky
Like a scythe for dark spirits

The archer's bow
Firing arrows of light around
The shiny stars.

Sam Fizor (9)
Churchdown Village Junior School

I Will Draw . . .

I will draw the glorious sight of an elegant horse,
galloping through a meadow in bloom.

I will draw the sound of the deep blue ocean waves,
crashing wildly against the cliff.

I will draw the relaxing aroma of lavender,
drifting gently around my plump pillow.

I will draw the caress of luxurious velvet,
concealing my sensitive skin.

I will draw the taste of a scrumptious square of chocolate,
melting speedily on my tongue.

Zoe Thomson (10)
Churchdown Village Junior School

My Hamster

My hamster is called Snowflake
I feed him every day
He likes to chew on nuts
But not a bale of hay

Snowflake has white fur
Black splodges too
If he were much bigger
He'd be a panda in a zoo

Snowflake is quite noisy
When he's keeping fit
He spins his wheel round and round
Then jumps into his pit

After he's been training
He's awake throughout the night
Then he sleeps through the daytime
I'm sure this can't be right

So Snowflake is my hamster
He also is my friend
Even though I love him
He drives me round the bend.

Jacob Fox (9)
Churchdown Village Junior School

Noisy Town

Lorries stamp through the busy town
Babies scream, 'Where are my parents?'
Cars skid on the icy tarmac
With full trains zooming past
What a busy, noisy town
We're out of here!

Melissa Davenport (8)
Churchdown Village Junior School

The Moon And Me

The moon stands like a silver cradle
With no baby resting inside
A curved icicle hanging by an invisible hook
In a dark cave of velvet night
An elephant's tusk ever glowing
By the sun's light
A gleaming smile
With bright shining teeth
But when the night ends
The sun grows immense and the moon disappears
Under an invisible cloak of light.

Olivia Yates (9)
Churchdown Village Junior School

Theatre School

Theatre school is so much fun,
When I'm there I can be anyone.
A boy, a girl, a horse or a dog,
Last time I was a warthog!
So how *do* you act 'fat and smelly
With a large protruding belly'?
Please don't talk about my tummy,
It really isn't very funny!
When you're at theatre school,
You can make lots of friends,
You can make a circle and play 'let's pretend!'

Jennifer Smee (8)
Churchdown Village Junior School

Nowhere

It happened two years ago on the 7th January
And from then on it began.

On the night before my birthday
Where was he to be seen? Nowhere!

On the night before Christmas
Where was he to be seen? Nowhere!

On the night before New Year
Where was he to be seen? Nowhere!

On the night before Easter
Where was he to be seen? Nowhere!

And then a year later
On a not so cold morning, the phone rang.

I answered sleepily to hear the voice
I had for so long dreamed to hear

The voice of he who is nowhere

My dad!

Laura Guest (8)
Churchdown Village Junior School

My Grandmother

My grandmother was a wonderful thing
My grandmother could dance and sing
My grandmother would hold me very tight
My grandmother could tell me stories all night
My grandmother is now in Heaven
I like to pretend she's just popped to Devon!

Bradley Tonks (8)
Churchdown Village Junior School

The Crescent Moon

The changing moon is like a
glowing slice of crystal, hanging
in the sky

A piece of a shattered mirror
reflecting a light bulb light

An old, bent silver pin which
once was new

A smile laughing with pearly-white teeth

The changing moon is like an
ever-glowing crescent shining in the middle
of a black curtain.

Jessica Smith (8)
Churchdown Village Junior School

Seasons

Spring is when all the beautiful daffodils grow,
Summer is when the sun shines like a disco ball,
Autumn is when all the leaves float to the ground and make
                                        a cosy carpet
Winter is when the snowflakes fall onto the frosty ground

Spring is when you dodge the April showers!
Summer is when you travel down to the beach
Autumn is when you gather all the leaves and have a leaf fight!
Winter is when *Santa* comes down the chimney
And makes every child happy!

Laura Jones (8)
Churchdown Village Junior School

Snow

Fluffy snow on the ground,
Where the animals lay low,
When the footballers frown,
A white blanket of snow.

Kids have fun,
All day long,
Acting like snow guns,
While some sing songs.

Wrap up warm,
It's going to be a cold one,
Cows nice and cosy at the farm,
Tomorrow will be fun.

Snow is fun for me and fun for you,
No time for rest,
Fun for you lot too,
Snow is the best.

Bill Clark (10)
Churchdown Village Junior School

My Bedroom

Bedrooms are messy, often not clean,
Toys scattered round,
Wallpaper ripped where monsters have been.

Clothes lying out, not in the wardrobe,
Paper and pens in a heap on the floor.
Everything out, not where it should be,
Teddies and rabbits all blocking the door.

My bedroom's tidy, everything in place,
Oh no, here's the Devil,
Oh no, he's emptied my case!

Hannah Carter (11)
Churchdown Village Junior School

The Night Devil

His hypnotic eyes
And sickening grin,
Snigger and hush,
While others sleep in.

Leaping dangerously,
Deciding not to care,
Slithering down chimneys
And no child is aware.

He delicately scoops up the boy
And stuffs him in his sack,
He plucks out a child of his own
And bounds out like a jumping jack.

The Devil child hisses at parents,
At the nothingness of night,
Screams, shudders and horror,
While the Devil laughs in delight.

The true one is shoved in groups
And terrorised with words I cannot share,
But the horrific vermin night-devil,
With his heart of stone never cares.

The young copies the father,
In a cunning, sinister way,
He spreads the chain of fungus,
Then millions of mischief lies here today.

His hypnotic eyes
And sickening grin,
Snigger and hush,
While others sleep in.

Beth Curtis (10)
Churchdown Village Junior School

Space

Why was there so much space?
Were we made to explore?
Are we alone in this place?
Do we want to see more?

Why do we have space?
What is the answer?
Is it in our face?
Do we have the power?

What is space?
Is it yours or mine?
Is it a race,
A race against time?

The answer, who knows!

Hannah Gibson (10)
Churchdown Village Junior School

Should We Talk . . . ?

'She's been standing there ever since she arrived,
With no special look,
I really think we ought to tell Miss,
She doesn't even read a book.'

'I don't think it's a good idea
To tell on her like that,
I think she wants to be left alone,
With the school's old cat.'

'Come on, let's tell,
She needs to be talked to, don't you see?
There's not much point in leaving her,
I know she needs help from me.'

'Fine, you go,
I'm leaving her alone,
Go on, I'm staying,
And anyway, she'll probably moan.'

Bethany Joy (10)
Churchdown Village Junior School

The Way The World Is

Once, I remember, far back in the past
The world was at peace and rest
Most people liked it, they thought it was great
And always was the very best

But then the greedy, selfish people
Wanted everything theirs, now
So war became the way of our lives
How were we to survive, how?

First came the great World War I
Then came World War II
Lots of innocent people died
All I say is true

You would have thought we'd stop wars
But this is what happened, this.
We continued fighting each other
That's just the way the world is.

Christine Badger (11)
Churchdown Village Junior School

Truly Magical

The moon shines,
Chimes its gleaming light,
For evermore,
Star-white.

The moon gleams,
Beams its light so bright,
Like something magical
In the night.

The moon fades,
Shades the pitch-black night,
Once again,
No light.

Katie Fryatt (8)
Churchdown Village Junior School

White Christmas

When I woke up
I saw a path
And it was white
I thought it was frost

I asked my mum
She said it was snow
I was amazed
It really was snow

I went outside
And ran about
I threw a snowball
And got one back

I went to bed
And thought of snow
When I woke up
The snow had *gone!*

Leonie Hammond (10)
Churchdown Village Junior School

Holidays

Holidays are really fun
And always full of laughter
Every time we go on holiday
We hope it's not disaster

The sand simmers
Lying in the sun
Splashing in the sea
Is very, very fun

Hotels are very joyful
You sleep, eat in them
You go out in the daytime
We always have fun.

Nicola Vizard (9)
Churchdown Village Junior School

The Butterflies

On a warm summer's day
In the garden we play
As the birds fly by
I see a beautiful butterfly

With an excited yell
Is that a tortoiseshell?
I think it may be
Next to that bumblebee

On its wings it has eyes
So it is no surprise
That a peacock we spy
I see a beautiful butterfly

Then from a greater height
Swoops a Cabbage White
It makes the Red Admiral
Look rather small

When a car drives by
They fly up high
In the blue, blue sky
I see a beautiful butterfly.

Emma Nield (8)
Churchdown Village Junior School

Me

I know a person who is . . .
Cooler than the coolest hippy,
Faster than Speedy Gonzales zooming across the motorway,
Greedier than a hamster stuffing its cheeks with food,
He is the weirdest person I know,
That person is . . . *me!*

Tom Batchelor (8)
Churchdown Village Junior School

Brussels Sprouts

'Open your mouth,' said my mum.
In went a great big green thing.
'#@"/***%&'-({}]@@#;!' I screamed
'What was that?'
'A sprout, dear,' my mother said.
'Well I ain't eatin' 'em again!'
And I think I made that rather clear.

When my sister, Emily, was 5 she'd say,
'Don't forget, *Brussels!'* and she'd say that at din-dins,
Even if din-dins had nothing to do with sprouts
And every Sunday din-dins
(As Sunday din-dins includes 'em)
Em (for that is what I called her) would say:
'67 Brussels for Vickikins (for that is what she called me) or more!'
Yet I can't understand why she says that because . . .
She's never tried one yet!

Victoria Weare (9)
Churchdown Village Junior School

Cakes

Cakes, cakes, glorious cakes
Swirling around in my head
Anywhere, everywhere, anytime too
I dream about them in my bed

Cakes, cakes, glorious cakes
They're going round flying
Rolling down a dreamy lane
I'm trying and just dying
To eat that cake!

April Salcombe (8)
Churchdown Village Junior School

Tomorrow

Tomorrow is another day,
With things to do and games to play,
So why not rest your sleepy head
And cuddle up to your ted?
In the morning there will be fun things
For you and me.

Edmund Rhys Jones (7)
Churchdown Village Junior School

Mean Machine

The adrenaline running through your veins
Saying, *'Stop! Can't handle the pain!'*
The bike screaming
'Don't hurt me
You won't be able to ride me again!'
You're loving the enjoyment of it
You can't stop until the juice runs out again.

Sam Broder (11)
Dursley Primary School

I Love And Hate

I love food and drink
I love the freedom to play
I love to go on holiday and
I love pocket money
I hate to go to bed early
I hate not being allowed to hit my brother
I hate not being allowed to lie.

Katy Greenhill (10)
Dursley Primary School

Sweetest To Devil

You're young, you have the rest of your life to live
And you could get away with murder, you're so cute and innocent.
That's when you're about 8, but when you get to 11
It all goes downhill.
You're a couple of years off being a teenager,
According to your parents are those things that smell
And listen to loud music all the time.
You suddenly turn into a devil; a rebellious creature
That doesn't love its parents and its aim in life is, apparently,
To go against its parents every wish.
Well, that's what they think.
They make you feel guilty about growing up by saying,
'See, I told you, you've got to that stage when
You don't love us and you don't want to be seen with us!'
Not true!
But then again you get more freedom.
Well you do over the minor things, like your clothes,
But they still have control of the things you really wish they didn't,
Like if you have a mobile, and, how long you stay up to watch a film,
But what they say about siblings hating each other isn't true,
I tell my sisters everything, I trust them and they trust me.

Harriet Coates (11)
Dursley Primary School

The Wind Howled

The wind howled like a pack of hungry wolves at night
The moon glared at me like a bloodthirsty zombie
The headstones lay ready to pounce at my every move
The branches stretched to try and grab me
They squeezed like a python
The fence posts pinched while the trees held me down
The wind led me to my dark death.

Nathan Pretty (10)
Dursley Primary School

The Skeleton's Shadow

The skeleton strolled along the corridor like a gangster,
Flames dancing in his eyes.
He stood still,
But his shadow was closing in on me.
I screamed but the shadow already had his spindly fingers
Round my throat.
The moonlight broke through the black velvet curtains.
A smirk on the moon's smug face.
There was a sleek black feline twisting round my skinny legs.
I felt the claws sink into my calves.
I looked into the cat's blood-red eyes
And it had a grin on its small face.
The shadow fingers tightened their grip around my neck.
The skeleton was laughing at my pain,
It was the last thing I ever heard.

Alice Wright (11)
Dursley Primary School

My Life

I like everything about being me
I like freedom to play
I like just being me
I like watching Sky Sports
But
I hate being looked after by other people
When my parents are at work
I hate my dad smacking me
I hate lying to my dad
I hate doing the washing up
Life's not a game when you're 10.

Jake Woods (11)
Dursley Primary School

I Have Freedom

Finally I have freedom
I have space from everyone
But why do I have to do SATs?
Can't I just miss out?
The good thing about it
I get to go on camp
I stay up later and make my own decisions
I can go out with my sister
And without Mum
We have loads of fun
Mum asks me more and I get a say in things
Why can't I play my music as loud as I like?
Why can't I go out after dark?
I won't get hurt
I thought you relied on me more.

Hollie Ind-Smith (11)
Dursley Primary School

Treated Differently!

I have freedom to play
But I hate being treated like a baby
And being treated like I'm never there
When I go out shopping, I can't buy anything I really want
But one day when I go to college
I can decide what I want to do as my career
I hate it when I get told off and when I get shouted at
It's just not fair, just because I have a little brother
That *never* gets told off
But when I'm at home, I can eat anything I want!
But my favourite snack is chocolate
And sweets.

Jennifer Wong (10)
Dursley Primary School

Motorbike!

It is my one and only dream
To have a fast machine
A huge Suzuki motorbike
Painted gleaming shiny green

On my bike on a 125
I would ride at great speed
All the way and everywhere
When I feel the greatest need

Down the windy lane I will ride
Going through the long green grass
A fantastic wheelie I will do
When I want to impress a lass

She could often sit and watch
While I would perform a really
Wonderful stunt in the dorm.

Jamie Griffey (10)
Dursley Primary School

Motorbikes!

I jump on my bike like a kangaroo
On the motorway now off goes my shoes
I ride past Burger King
Then I realise I've rode on a pin
I saw a car on the road
Shouting as he drove
I saw a man drinking pop
As he came out the local shop

It's becoming night now
So I best take a bow
I parked my bike in my house
Then fed my pet mouse.

Aaron Darlow (10)
Dursley Primary School

The Meaning Of Life!

I love being a kid,
because you get lots of presents,
you have a loving family
and your own TV.
But you haven't even heard the good bits yet,
'What?' I hear you say, 'Something better than TV.'
Yes, there is something better than TV,
like buying sweets or having a home.

But everything has a downside,
even absolute freedom has its downs,
some of the downs are like not being allowed to stay up late
or not being able to raid the food cupboard.
But the worst thing of all is being overpowered by your parents
or other adults, so you have to act like a puppet on strings,
doing your parents' dirty work.
So I think it's better to grow up and discover the meaning of life.

Benjamin Lewis (10)
Dursley Primary School

My Lifetime

I love getting attention
It makes me proud of
The things I do
It's good being young
Watching TV and
Sitting around instead
Of doing jobs
Sport's really fun when
I'm playing football or running
Because I'm
Always doing well.

Ella Hitchcox (10)
Dursley Primary School

Team Spirit

Team spirits keeps you alive
It will help you come through, through and thrive
If you get injured, don't let your head drop
Now and then you'll get a small knock

Passion is everything
You'd do anything for a win
The players aren't emotional
They are just like raging bulls

You must be tough
And be prepared to play rough
You must come along and play
Come along and play today.

Simon Thomas (10)
Dursley Primary School

Freedom

I like freedom to play
We get to go on adventure camps
I like chocolate
Responsibilities of growing up
Lack of independence
Good films I cannot watch
I want to be taller
I hate to go to bed early.

Lara Lovegrove (11)
Dursley Primary School

The Way Things Always Go

I always get the blame,
Although I'm not tame,
But this is unfair,
Best films not allowed,
Because they are always 18s.

But there are better things about it,
Like getting more responsibility
And exploring the countryside
Around you more,
But that's not all.

It's getting to find some history
And the partying all night,
But none of that's my favourite yet!
It's doing bell ringing and hockey for 2 hours.

Emily Lyons (10)
Dursley Primary School

The Cell Door

The cell door howled
Waiting impatiently to swallow an unworthy
Devouring him whole.
He cries a pitiful cry
Shouting every word imaginable
Then darkness comes upon him.
He prays as death teases his lonely body
His body white with frost
Darkness takes him
And his carcass gradually rots away
Leaving nothing but bones.

Jake Cooke
Dursley Primary School

Kid Aged 11

They say you're only young once,
Being a kid is not always easy,
The decisions you have to make,
When it's all over,
It's not much fun anymore,
It feels like time is a dream.

The freedom I have,
The independence is the best thing about me.

The bad things about being a kid
Are one day you're grown up
And everything you have will soon be lost.

But although sometimes it's not all great,
I wouldn't swap it for anything,
Being a kid is special.

Kirsty Reynolds (11)
Dursley Primary School

The Tidal Wave

Birds cheeping, shadows creeping
The sun gleaming upon windows
Teachers talking, children chatting
I saw a gliding buzzard soaring in the sky
All was silent . . .
Boom! The children poured out
Like a giant tidal wave in a calm, still ocean
Children shouting, teachers counting.

Robert Bartlett
Dursley Primary School

Being A Kid

I hate being looked after by other people
They always want to watch what they want
And they say I'm not allowed to play
I'm not being a slave
My only dream is to drive a car
I always get the blame.

Rebecca Carrier (10)
Dursley Primary School

Cool Child

I hate lack of things to do and places to go
I have time for freedom to play
I have one annoying brother in one room
And I'm in the other room and I can hear him shouting
I love chocolate and sweets
People think that it's easy being a kid
Now I have my own responsibilities of growing up.

Rebecca Crane (10)
Dursley Primary School

I Like Playing

I like playing football
Football is my talent
Rugby is mine too
Hockey comes up
But I love playing football
Football is my talent
And that's what I do.

Jake Williams (11)
Dursley Primary School

A Mythical Battle Of Mythical Might

The Basilisk eyed its victim with both heads
The Sphinx was crouched and ready
The Sta's eyes were on the Griffin
And the moves of the Axex unsteady

Anubis was first to fall
He met the Basilisk eye to eye
That is what caused him to die!

But the Basilisk's lethal eyes were met
By the Sphinx's sandy claws
Not the sort of picture a child draws

With magnificent wings of purple and pink
The only flyer was Griffin
The others laughed at the colours so he squawked 'Don't get dissin''

The Sta and the Axex ran away . . .
To be met by booby traps
Ha, that stopped them in their tracks!

The Sta let out a yelp and ran
Right into sinking sand!
Now there was a rope but he had no hands!

With a valiant effort the Griffin tried
To be a hero but failed
His quest availed

With the Axex gone
There was a winner, the Sphinx
But his skin was dimmer!

Kenny Smith (11)
Dursley Primary School

Being Babied!

Don't you just hate being babied?
They squeeze you tight
They call you annoying names
Like Sweetpea, Angel, My Baby and worst, Honeykins
But if you stop and *think*
They love you
They buy you whatever you ask for
You're innocent to everything
You're the youngest, cutest, most harmless thing in your family
And that's great!

But when you get to ten (or older)
Your parents think you're stressy
Monsters and smelly ogres
You get blamed for almost anything
Seen as noisy, ugly, bloodsucking creatures
And that's not great!

Katherine Hamilton
Dursley Primary School

The Seal Sanctuary

I was on the roaring Land Rover
Down the hill we went
Watching the seals flapping their flippers
And searching for food

They search and search until they find some
The seals gave me a headache
So I went to the wood for a walk
And then we looked up to a cage of lions
And a pool of penguins.

Aaron Powick (9)
Field Court Junior School

Safari Park

First we saw the monkeys, they were really funny,
Damaging cars, destroying them as if they wanted money,
Next we saw the elephants,
Rolling in the mud, spraying water everywhere,
What big mucky pups,
Then we saw the lions, they were very loud,
Scaring me to pieces,
I wanted to get out.

Afterwards the tigers
Climbing on the car, they took a long time to get off
And then we went on,
Finally the giraffes,
Eating leaves off the trees,
Goodbye all you animals,
It's time for us to leave.

Samuel Digby (9)
Field Court Junior School

The Zoo

As I walk through the zoo
I see the lion's den
The lion roars
And I see his massive paws
With its giant claws

I look at the monkeys
Just as I have to go
I run back through the wild zoo
Like a madman.

Liam Wallwork-Gush (10)
Field Court Junior School

Animals And Me

Cats sleep soundly
Dogs bark loudly
Hamsters stroll proudly
But I walk gladly

Cats eat cat food
Dogs eat dog food
Hamsters eat hamster food
But I eat my food!

Holly Carrick (10)
Field Court Junior School

Farm

As I see the muddy farm
I hear tons of noise
I smell the smell of a typical farm
That makes me want to run

The mud squishes around my shoes
That makes noises so bad
The smell of the smelly place
Makes me want to be in a race.

Aaron Meredith (10)
Field Court Junior School

My School

My school is a place where I feel happy and calm
It is small but
I don't mind because
It has lovely colourful displays!

It is bright but my friends are peaceful
I hear children and teachers
And it is nothing but the best!

Connar Westgate (10)
Field Court Junior School

Gloucester Cathedral

As I walked up to Gloucester cathedral,
I held onto my mum,
I saw stone coffins
And lots of magical Monks

It looked so big and ancient,
I felt as little as a mouse,
I wanted to go home,
Straight back to my house.

Joshua Etherton (9)
Field Court Junior School

Blackpool

As I walked into the park,
I think all about the rides,
I know I'll go on one,
I just might fall off the sides.

I'm going home now,
The day is at an end,
I wish it didn't go so quick,
It's all gone round the bend.

Gemma King (10)
Field Court Junior School

Town Centres

As I walk along the streets,
I'm feeling very calm,
I smell the smell of fast food
And I hear a car alarm.

The wind is whipping,
Around my nose,
In the shop I hear peaceful music
And it makes me want to doze.

Callum Marshall (9)
Field Court Junior School

Drayton Manor

As I walked into the park
I heard a lot of screams
As it was so gigantic
It felt like a dream

I jumped onto a ride
It gave me quite a shock
It was just so fast
I felt I couldn't stop

It's time to go home
It was an adventurous day
The rides were just amazing
But I forgot to pay!

Rebecca Burrows (9)
Field Court Junior School

My House

As I strolled through my front door,
I was cheerful and pleased to see my parents,
All I could smell was cooking,
It smelt delicious,
I walked into the living room.

All I could see was sofas and a TV,
The TV was wide and big
And the sofas were warm, cosy and comfortable.
I gracefully walked to the bathroom,
Which had a bath, toilet and a sink.
I went to my bedroom to lie on my bed,
Which was cosy, comfortable and warm.

Kimberley Brooks (10)
Field Court Junior School

At The Beach

Lollipops dripping as quickly as running water,
Jellyfish zipping this way and that,
At the beach, at the beach.

Slimy, sludgy sand,
White cliffs crumbling away,
At the beach, at the beach.

Clapping seals,
Jumping fish,
At the beach, at the beach.

Seagulls pinching food to eat,
People making skyscrapers out of sand,
At the beach, at the beach.

Zoe Bartholomew (9)
Field Court Junior School

Seaside

I can hear waves
And children talking,
The birds are squawking too,
The cliffs are tall,
The wind is rising,
The water is deep,
I feel safe, warm and pleased.

I can smell the food,
The hot dogs and drinks,
I ran and looked for some more,
But something stopped me,
I thought, it was the end of my dream holiday.

Shannon Newcombe (10)
Field Court Junior School

As I Walk Along The Beach

As I walk along the beach, the golden sand
I feel the sun beam
I see children making sandcastles
And I lick my ice cream

As I swim into the sea
I can feel the slimy seaweed
I can taste salt in the water
A bag of chips is all I need.

Summer Hynam (9)
Field Court Junior School

My Sandy Wonderland

As I run along the golden sand,
I feel the warm grains underfoot,
I hear the rumble of the sea
And a feeling of happiness comes to me.

As I splash in the sea,
Whilst licking my ice cream,
I see some children playing
And it makes me want to sing.

Kayleigh Hather (10)
Field Court Junior School

Seaside

As I stroll across the seaside
I wonder what I might see
The tide coming in
Or surfers in the sea

As I stroll across the seaside
I wonder what I might smell
Hot dogs, burgers, chips or drinks
Or maybe some ice cream as well.

Ryan Greenwood (10)
Field Court Junior School

A Theme Park

The moment I went to the theme park,
The parade, the rides, the noise
Surrounds me
Everywhere I go.

I patted, I smelt
I ate the food and the people I saw
Screaming on the rides,
I think I want a try!

Zoë Jenner (10)
Field Court Junior School

Theme Park

When I first walked into the park
I saw chips,
It was really exciting,
When I got onto the water slide
I saw mad people going in
And out of the pool,
At once I got out
And I got some chips.

Gregory Gibbs (9)
Field Court Junior School

In The Sea

Waves splashing and crashing on the rocks,
Sand softly blowing against the wall,
Dogs barking at the crackling seagulls,
Children playing on the sand,
Fish jumping as high as a kite,
Boats calmly sailing on the sea.

Lauren Ferris (8)
Field Court Junior School

The Seaside

Shimmering shells
Dancing donkeys
Salty sea
Prancing ponies

Fish and chips
Sandcastles
Buckets and spades
Grey seagulls, shouting children, fluffy blankets
Coloured umbrellas

Sea stars
Reef raiders
Loads of cars

White whales
When it sails
It whacks its tail.

Kayleigh Fryer (8)
Field Court Junior School

The Slide

As I walk into the park
I want to go on the slide
I begged my mum
She said, 'Yes, stop being a pest'
I walked to the slide
And asked for a ride
The man said, 'Yes, go on the slide'

I climbed on the slide
And I remembered I am afraid of heights!

Jake Butt (10)
Field Court Junior School

Seaside

As I walked along the soft sand
I could hear the children playing happily
There were waves crashing against the jagged rocks
I heard seagulls crying
I saw boats sailing

The sea was as blue as the sky
I saw sandcastles
It was so joyful
I smelt food
Hot dogs, burgers and drinks
But I began home again.

Abigail Humphris (9)
Field Court Junior School

The Seaside

The waves were hitting and running
The wind was blowing against my face
The birds were flying
And I was splashing
I was jumping up and down
My friends were running
But I was watching them build castles

When they finished I ran and ran
And broke the castle down
We caught a fish and put it back
And that's my holiday gone.

Charlie Gardiner (9)
Field Court Junior School

Sweet Spring

Sweet spring, sweet spring,
When all the lambs are born
And the rays of sunshine
Are the colour of corn.

The pink and green buds,
Bursting from the brown and green trees
And the daffodils, daisies, primroses
And crocuses are poking their heads
Above the fresh green grass.

Butterflies and bees dance and sing
In the breeze,
Birds are stunning
And squirrels are cunning.

Everything is nice in spring,
It really makes your heart sing!
Sweet spring, sweet spring.

Georgia Crisp (8)
Field Court Junior School

The Seaside Is Fun

A gushing sea with jumping jellyfish
Soft silky sand and gunky mud
And soaring seagulls soaring over here,
Soaring over there, soaring everywhere!
And the shipwrecks smelling musty and old
On the crooked rocks and the sparkling corals in the sea's tide
With the blazing sun in the horizon
With a blue sky in the background
With speedboats zooming across the water.

Josh Bingham (8)
Field Court Junior School

The Iron Rat

He scampers around the house,
Chasing the fat mouse,
He moves angrily stomping around,
All over the ground,
Oh, he's waiting to . . . bang your knee.

In a dark hole,
He lives with a mole,
He hides under the table,
With a toy stable,
Oh, he's waiting to . . . bang your knee.

His iron body,
(Fooling everybody),
Shimmering in the sunlight,
With his iron knuckles ready to fight,
His head madly nodding,
Oh, he's waiting to . . . bang your knee.

Sean Jarrett (9)
Field Court Junior School

The Seaside

Popping sand,
Little orange clownfish,
Swimming in the sea,
Man of war floating poisonously
On top of the sea,
Swishing seaweed,
Sparkling shells as smooth as marble,
Great white shark searching for food,
Dolphins diving in and out of the ocean,
Stormy waves.

Joshua Hayward (8)
Field Court Junior School

The Nasty Monster

My monster is purple with spots that are pink,
His teeth are blue just like the colour of ink,
His claws are thick and sharp,
For he's waiting . . . just waiting to get you.

The grumpy monster stomps so loud,
As the noise goes up to the clouds,
Sometimes he drags his feet in the street,
For he's waiting . . . just waiting to get you.

The horrible monster lives in a flat,
With Rosie, the pussy cat.
His flat is small but is full of old witches,
For he's waiting . . . just waiting to get you.

The huge monster eats orange beans,
But also he likes to eat jeans,
He will eat mostly anything,
For he's waiting . . . just waiting to get you.

Lauren Alps (8)
Field Court Junior School

Once Upon A Rhyme

Once upon a rhyme
In a land before time
Little Bo-Peep has lost her sheep
And the Riddle Robbers have done a crime.

Humpty Dumpty has fallen off his wall
And the gingerbread man thinks he's small
What a funny little town!

Phoebe Embling (8)
Field Court Junior School

The Ankle Grabber

Every night under your bed
The Ankle Grabber's scaly head
Appears from under your nest
Oh he's waiting . . . just waiting . . . to grab you!

When he slithers through the night
He grabs every ankle in his sight
He pulls them down into his dark lair
For he's waiting . . . and watching . . . and waiting there!

As he likes the ankles so much
His mother says, 'Don't you dare touch!'
But as he always disobeys
Oh yes he's waiting . . . just waiting . . . for you!

They say he may come from the planet Mars,
Which is surrounded by many bright, shining stars
And has caves which they say are very large
Where he's waiting . . . just waiting . . . to get you!

Be very afraid and be aware
Should you approach his evil lair,
For he may, by chance, be waiting there
Oh he's waiting . . . just waiting . . . to get you!

When life on Earth has come and gone
The Ankle Grabber lingers on,
To make you shout and sweat and scream
As he infests your darkest dream.

Dawn Barlow (9)
Field Court Junior School

Water Wonders

Shining fish,
Gliding seagulls,
Humming whales,
Jumping dolphins,
These are the beauties of the sea!

Salty water,
Aggressive crabs,
Swimming people,
Transparent sea,
These are the beauties of the sea!

The sea is wonderful!

Daniel Westgate (8)
Field Court Junior School

At The Seaside

Coconuts as hairy as a gorilla,
Glimmering stars dancing on the sea,
A massive whale moved swiftly in the salty water,
See the smooth pebbles,
Great jumping jellyfish,
Slippery slimy seaweed,
Slender twilight caves
Seaside beach,
Seaside beach
What a wonderful place to be!

Scott Oram (8)
Field Court Junior School

Once Upon A Rhyme

Sat down here
Feeling fine
Haven't got a lot of time
Under the table
Beaty is asleep
Now and again
She has a little peep
Her supper has not arrived
But her toys are by her side
Under the table is her bed
She lies there, the big old sleepyhead
Sometimes she gives a snort and a growl
She has been known to bark and howl!

Chloe Buckley (8)
Field Court Junior School

Golden Sand

Golden sand as soft as carpet
Sparkling shells shimmering
Snapping crabs in a rock pool
Climbing smooth glassy pebbles
Squawking seagulls gliding over the ocean
A tidal wave as big as a hotel dashing over the sand,
Jumping dolphins as happy as a party
The golden sand lights up like a frying pan
The rustling of a shell
Hear the shell speak
It's good as good can be.

Hannah Orchard (8)
Field Court Junior School

Electricity

Electricity is dangerous
Water and electric - *boom!*
Don't mess around
Or you will meet your doom!

If you get an electric shock
Don't fuss and roll around
If you have rubber shoes
It'll go straight through the ground!

Don't chew a wire
It'll make you jump
Watch out for the gunfire
You will jump and bump!

Make sure you don't play with electric
So you won't get electric shocks
Your parents won't go bonkers
Electric should have locks!

Michael Poat (9)
Field Court Junior School

The Seaside

The gloomy, whizzing, blue sea
Mrs Smallwood is as angry as a tiger
The zapping electric eels

The gooey slippery sand
The shimmering stars danced on the water
The calm blue sea

The waves blushing in the powerful wind
The smell of the old seaweed
The sound of seagulls on the gloomy sea.

Charlotte Emery (9)
Field Court Junior School

Just Guess!

A donkey to ring a bell,
A parrot to tell,
An eel to turn on the light,
A dog to hoover the floor, well he might.

Just guess, what animals are going to be next?
The lion is king of text.

A cheetah to teach PE,
Well he taught me,
A spider to be a dinner lady,
That was crazy.

Just guess, what animals are going to be next?

Serena Deakins (8)
Field Court Junior School

Australia

Hot and dusty plains
Silent with a gentle breeze
Brushing the sand over my footsteps

Not a person in sight
Boiling hot sand under my feet
A blazing hot sun with a light cloudless sky

Everyone is out playing
But in the night it gets freezing
And silent with the occasional flutter from a flock of birds.

Dean Pearce (9)
Field Court Junior School

Silver Fang, The Ice Wolf

The call of the wild from the pack of the fang boss,
The thick snowy paw prints left on the ground
Silver, thick-coated fur all around
Teeth, claws, paws
Drags the cold-blooded food along the floor
The cold ice wings and ice down his neck
With decorated ice paws and the head shield
The cold old wolf sprints like a spear
The call from the boss; the pack await you!

Jason Burt (9)
Field Court Junior School

Theme Park

Padding past the giant rides wondering what to do
Smelling all the tasty food, looking for the loo
Excited of all the rides, looking at things, what to do
Other people walking around, looking as excited as I am

Watching all the candyfloss spinning round and round
I was walking round the park then I found a pound
I saw a spinning wheel almost touching the ground.

Ryan Butt (10)
Field Court Junior School

Me

Some people think I am silly,
Some people think I am skinny,
Some people think I am fat,
Some people think I look like a cat,
Some people think I am smart and good at art,
But I just think that I am going to be *me!*

Sophie Barton (8)
Field Court Junior School

The Girl

Night was cold, the trees were creaking,
I heard a voice of someone speaking,
I was on my own, it made me shiver,
I tried to stand in quiver.

Suddenly the glow,
Shone in like a massive blow,
Still nothing,
Then someone stepped into the light.

She was see-through,
I closed my eyes, it couldn't be true.
She started walking forward,
Then vanished.

The next night,
She gave me a fright.
She stood before me,
Looking gory.

Emily Stevens (11)
Hillview CP School

Creepy Poetry

It was a cold and gloomy night
And when there was a knock at the window
I had such a fright

I ran out of my room into the midnight gloom
And on the floor was a broken down door
How it got there I did not know
So I went to look for footprints out in the snow

Nothing was found out on the snowy ground
So I went back to bed and snuggled up with my ted.

Rebecca Wyse (10)
Hillview CP School

The Fright On Friday Night

Suddenly there was a knock at the door,
I fell out of bed and onto the floor,
He came upstairs to rip me apart,
Scattered my guts like a piece of art.

My mum came in without a head,
She dropped to the floor completely dead,
My dad went downstairs to have a drink,
But the man was sitting in my sink.

My brother smashed a bottle of beer,
Slashed the man's face and let out a cheer.
The man fell to join the dirt,
Then I realised he was wearing a skirt.

He wasn't a man after all,
He was a girl, slim and tall.
My brother turned to see a ghost,
Who was charging at him with a lamp post.

The ghost killed him with such force,
The only survivor was my dog, Morse.

H Crosby
Hillview CP School

Creepy Poetry

It was midnight and something wasn't right,
I turned on the light and went downstairs to have a bite,
I went to the tap to get a drink
But all I could see was a blood-filled sink,
I turned around and to my surprise
I saw a big fat guy eating my pies
He sharpened his knife ready to kill
But on his jumper it said his name was Bill
They mentioned his name on killer TV
All I had to do was give him some tea.

Sean West
Hillview CP School

Creepy Poetry

People say he's just a dream,
But if they saw him, they would scream.
He creeps around with a certain sound,
Through the trees and all around.

He will come at the dead of night,
Especially to give you a great big fright.
No doubt that you would be so scared,
Certainly, definitely, unprepared.

No matter what you try to do,
He will keep his eye on you.
You can hide or run away,
But he will catch you anyway.

You now know what I'm talking about,
No matter what he'll catch you out.
Now you can run to your loving mum,
But she won't be there when he comes.

Anwen Carter (11)
Hillview CP School

Creepy Poetry

Me and my brother were in our bedroom and we looked at the sky
Heard a moan and a groan from the deep dark wood and
I started to cry
So I went to my dad and he came to my room
And he opened the curtains - nothing to be seen till noon

So the next night my dad stayed
Up with us then we prayed
That it might just go away
We so hoped it would not stay

The dream was a warning
And now I think it's the morning
But my brother is still snoring
No wonder it's early and I'm still yawning!

James Russell (10)
Hillview CP School

What Is That?

What's tapping in the middle of the night?
I don't know, but it gave me a fright!
I thought it was someone speaking,
However, it was just the door creaking.

It was outside the door,
On the floor.
I heard a quiet tap,
It might be the cat flap.

He creeps around,
Without a sound,
At the dead of night,
That takes you out of sight.

I thought I heard a scream,
But it might just be my dream,
Just then my mum came in
And gave me a grin.

Alice Watkins (11)
Hillview CP School

Creepy Poetry

When the floorboards creak and hinges squeak,
When the TV's off but seems to speak,
When the moon is full and you hear a shriek.

When the spiders gather beneath your bed,
When they colonise the garden shed,
When they spin their webs right above your head.

When the lights are out and there's no one home,
When you're by yourself and you're on your own,
When the radiators bubble and groan.

Something lurking in the night,
Ready to give me a fright,
Creaking floorboards when I turn off the light
And just hope that it's Mum come to see that you're alright.

Tashan Vadher
Hillview CP School

The Fright On Monday Night

I was lying in my bed on Monday night,
When I got a sudden fright,
So I went downstairs to get a drink,
Then I saw a man drinking out of my sink.

The moonlight beamed on the man,
So I threw a can,
The can hit him in the head,
So he fell to the floor dead.

I screamed as I ran upstairs really scared
And then I got prepared,
Another man came up the stairs and kicked my cat,
She went flying onto the tattered mat.

I woke up in the morning with sleep in my eyes,
So I went downstairs to get a pie,
I found a dead man on the floor,
So I walked over him and went out the door.

Daniel Hill (11)
Hillview CP School

Creepy Poetry

The clock had just struck strangely 12 midnight
It woke me up and gave me a fright
Then I went downstairs to the loo
And something went 'Boo!'

I went upstairs to my room
There was a big bang *boom!*
I turned on the light and gave myself a fright.

Hey you there, beware
You will be in for a scare . . .

Kayne Cook
Hillview CP School

Creepy Poetry

The night was dim and I gave a sigh,
I hid under my covers as I gave a little cry.
As someone was speaking while I was asleep,
As the floor was creaking.

The litter bin was blowing in the wind,
As the wind taps and tapping,
Who is searching in my home?
Like a big mouse.

I got out of my bed
And there was a ghost
Under my bedcover,
When my mum came in.

I went to the toilet
And I saw a ghost in the bathroom,
I screamed and my mum came in
And my big brother.

At first I was really scared,
Because I was underpaid,
But then I found out that it was my mum,
I'm safe at last, I'm safe at home.

She takes me to her bed
And makes me a drink
I go to sleep
And I had a funny feeling.

Tracie Grieve (11)
Hillview CP School

Creepy Poetry

It was a cold, dark night,
When the wind gave me a fright.
Someone was speaking,
The floor was creaking.

The letterbox flapped,
As the window tapped.
Under the covers I hide,
When the curtains glide.

By the post,
There was a ghost,
Who searched the house
Like some big mouse.

I got out of bed
And there instead,
Was my mother
And my big brother.

At first I was really scared
Because I was unprepared.
But then I found it was my mum,
So now I am safe at home.

She tucked me up tight in bed,
I had a cold feeling in my head.
Soon I glided off to sleep,
Under my nice warm sheets.

Laura Faulkner (10)
Hillview CP School

Creepy Poetry

It was a cold, dark night,
Although there was a bit of light,
As I went to sleep,
I heard a creep.

The floor was creaking,
When I heard someone speaking,
Then I said it was a dream,
But then I heard a scream.

It knocked on the door
And slid on the floor,
It gave me some post,
I opened it, it was a ghost.

I got out of bed
And it ran away instead,
I called for my mum,
She wouldn't come.

I found her fast asleep,
I couldn't hear anymore creeps,
I didn't do anymore screams,
Then I had a nice dream.

Lucie Allen (11)
Hillview CP School

Creepy Poetry

It was a dark and scary night
I had a really scary fright
There were people speaking
And floorboards creaking

I switched on the light and had a scare
To find an alien that lifted my hair
I heard the mailman deliver the post
To me I thought it was a ghost

I opened my door
And looked at the floor
It was covered in snakes
That looked like a lake

I heard the door *a-rat-a-tat-tat*
But I said to myself, *it's only a cat*
It was very daunting
I was sure she was haunting

I thought to myself, *I am only dreaming*
But then I heard her screaming
I ran upstairs to hide away
And she's been stalking me until this day.

Krystal Ricketts
Hillview CP School

Sunday Night Fright

I was lying in my room all on my own,
I heard this really creepy groan,
It came through the door and across the floor
And then I heard a knock at the door.

I went downstairs to get a drink,
And a man was sitting in my sink,
He sharpened his knife after killing his wife,
So I went back to bed to clear my head.

I went downstairs unprepared,
While feeling very scared
And then there was a knock at the door,
In came the ghost of poor Thomas Moore

And then I realised it was just a dream
And how cruel my mind had been,
So I went back to bed to clear my head
And in the morning the house was dead.

Samuel Wheeler (11)
Hillview CP School

Sunday Night Fright!

I was lying in bed one Sunday night,
The knock on the door gave me quite a fright,
I went downstairs and found a man,
Then I hit him with a frying pan.

He lay on the floor like a piece of dirt
And then I realised he was wearing a skirt.
It wasn't a man after all,
Just a woman, very tall.

Slowly the woman got up,
Then I killed her with a cup.
It smashed into pieces on her head,
She lay on the floor completely dead.

Her husband came running in,
Then I stabbed him with a pin,
I went upstairs and jumped on my bed,
I lay there in silence to clear my head.

George Batt (11)
Hillview CP School

Creepy Poetry

One night a girl went to bed
Unaware that under her head
Such monsters creep
To scare her off her feet

She went downstairs that night
To have a nibble and a bite
She turned on the TV
And to her eyes she believed

A girl gliding out the TV
And started crawling on her knees
She became so scared she had a fright
And ran out in the dead of night

She woke up, it was a dream
She went downstairs to have some ice cream
Then she turned on the TV
And there was a girl, so she believed . . .

Emily Prince & Hannah Dewick (11)
Hillview CP School

Your Worst Nightmare

It was night
I got a fright
The window was tapping
The curtains were flapping

I heard a scream
It came from the stream
I heard someone speak
Then the floorboards creak

At the door I stared
I got really scared
I heard the floor
Then I saw the door

Then I woke up to
Coffee in a cup
I had a bad scare
Now I'm back in good care.

Liam Long (10)
Hillview CP School

One Night!

One night I had such a fright,
When I woke up in the middle of the night,
The floorboards were making creaking noises,
But also outside I could hear people's voices!

One night I woke up and started to stare,
I suddenly felt a bit scared,
But when I looked out my room, there was nothing there,
Just me in the pitch-black!

One night it was quite dark
And I woke up with a start,
I thought I heard something lurking, so I got up to have a peep,
To find that everyone else was asleep!

One night I was fast asleep,
But then I felt a creep,
When I thought I felt my door close,
I woke up and nothing was there!

That night I was unprepared,
But I'll admit I was quite scared
And I found out that it was the window open,
So all I was startled by was the wind!

Lauren Smith (11)
Hillview CP School

Creepy Poetry

It was a dark and scary night,
When I had quite a fright,
To see an alien, it lifted my hair,
It was really ugly so it gave me a scare.

I heard people speaking
And floorboards were creaking,
It was really daunting,
I'm sure it would be haunting.

It was now late at night and I was asleep,
I heard something groaning so I had a peep.
There were ghosts in my hallway
And in my mum's doorway.

I heard the dripping of the tap,
But it was only a cat,
I heard something on the floor,
So I quickly ran and slammed the door.

That night I was scared,
Because I was unprepared.
It was only a horror I had dreamed,
Now I was safe home it seemed.

Megan Goode (10)
Hillview CP School

Creepy Poetry

I was lying in my bed one night,
When suddenly I got a fright.
I heard some creaking,
Then someone speaking.

I crept downstairs,
Unprepared,
But then I saw a lobster,
That looked like a monster.

I ran to the door,
But fell to the floor.
I hurt my head,
It went all red.

I got up and threw something at him
And he landed in the bin,
I went into my room and put on my hat,
Hoping that was the end of that!

Matthew Davis (10)
Hillview CP School

The Crab

His claws are sharper than a sword in flames,
His eyes are shinier than the ripples of the sea shivering silently,
He's faster than the wind blowing in an autumn breeze
And slimier than seaweed on rocks of the ocean shore,
He's meaner than a dog when it spies a cat
And rougher than a storm blowing all the leaves off the trees,
Slyer than a fox in a calm meadow,
His body is shinier than glass in the ocean,
Rounder than a neatly cut circle in line with another circle
And almost wetter than the sea lapping over the rocks.

Ethan Buxton (9)
Lakeside Primary School

Revel - Rebel

Go to school whenever I like,
When I go ride my bike,
What's the point in closing the gate?
Because that is the job I hate,
Don't let anyone say I'm wrong,
Go on the computer all day long,
Why should I put things back on the shelf
When I have the house to myself?
Order a pizza, can't be bothered to cook,
Play loud music, won't read a book,
Whenever I go and see my mate,
They always complain because I'm late,
Don't anyone tell me to be quiet,
Or anyone tell me to go on a diet,
Leave the dishes all scattered about,
When the bell goes scream and shout,
Play my CDs all day long,
Sing when it's my favourite song,
Never go on walks in the hills,
Always go on mega thrills,
That is because I revel,
In being a little rebel.

Joanne Crisp (10)
Lakeside Primary School

Cobwebs

Frosty cobwebs on the icy hedge,
The cobwebs look like tinsel on a Christmas tree,
Or tiny clouds in the blue sky,
The sun creeps upon the glittering white frost,
Melts away like ice cream on a hot day,
Slowly the spider walks across its shiny new web,
While the golden sun rises.

Lucy Bartrick (11)
Lakeside Primary School

Summer In The Country

As the bright blue cornflowers grow,
The gurgling spring rushes and flows,
As the fairies dance and twirl,
The petal's leaves quietly uncurl.

As the ivy creeps along,
The sunflowers grow proud and strong,
As the willows droop and swing,
The evergreen grows as proud as a king.

As the cat stalks through the bushes,
The ducks go quack in the rushes,
As the lolloping bunny's peer,
The chestnut Arabs whinny and rear.

As the lake gleams in the sunlight,
The children fly their dragon kite,
As the bird soars overhead I realise it's an eagle,
The spaniel runs through the beagles.

Kayleigh Tompkins (9)
Lakeside Primary School

I Wish I Had A Plate

I wish I had sweets
And some cheese
And macaroni and peas
And I would love to have lots of peas please

I wish I had some chips
And some sweets
And lots of biscuits
And I would love to have lots of treats.

Abigail Stacey (7)
Lakeside Primary School

Lakeside School

The bell rings for another new day,
Everybody rushes inside, no time to play,
Coats on pegs, bags on books,
Children sit down with their hooks.

Morning assembly in the school hall,
Is a time to sing - one and all.
Announcements are made, so much to say,
Mr Van Den Brock would be training yet another day.

There is lots to learn, so much to do,
We travel the world but not in a car,
Through Greece, Rome, Europe and Africa.

Spelling, tables and punctuation,
All need to be learnt by the nation,
Along the way we learn about us,
That is just a bit of what school does.

Jessica Halsall (9)
Lakeside Primary School

All Things Were Black

I used to think all things were black
Until I saw an old country shack
I used to think all things were blue
Until I looked down the loo
I used to think all things were red
Until I saw a four poster bed
I used to think all things were pink
Until I looked at the soap in the sink
And now I know the world has colour
If it didn't, it would be much duller.

Jonathan Morris (10)
Lakeside Primary School

Gruesome Greens!

My mum makes me eat my vegetables,
And I think that's so unfair,
Because I have a best friend called Louise
And *her* mum doesn't care

My sister thinks I'm really silly
Making such a fuss
But she doesn't know what it feels like
To have to eat that mush

Dad makes me eat *all m*y sprouts
Even on Christmas Day!
I think it's better to give than to receive
So I gave my sprouts away

My mum wasn't too happy
When she found them on her plate
She grounded me for a whole month
So I couldn't see my mates

My brother said sprouts would make me grow
But my dad ate all mine
Now I know that he was right
And that's why I'm still nine!

Kate Dickinson (9)
Lakeside Primary School

Untitled

I wonder where the birds have gone
Now that winter's here?
We never hear the songs they sing
Which brings us such cheer
We are pleased to say they will return
When the winter's done.

Evie Page (8)
Lakeside Primary School

In The Jungle

In the jungle
Monkeys mess madly,
Gorillas grumble gladly,
Elephants eat endlessly,
Snakes slither sadly.

Tigers tread triumphantly,
Spiders scrawl scarily,
Leopards leap lively,
Lions lurk lifelessly.

Ants annoy aggressively,
Chameleons crawl cautiously,
Rhinos run noisily
Gibbons glide gracefully

In the jungle
Monkeys mess madly
Gorillas grumble gladly
What a great place to be!

Roxana Shafiee (10)
Lakeside Primary School

Under The Sea

Under the sea,
Dolphins dive daringly,
Sharks swim sparingly,
Coral calls cautiously,
Seaweed sways soundlessly,
Crabs creep carelessly,
Lobsters loll lifelessly,
Under the sea is certainly lively.

Beverley Fricker (10)
Lakeside Primary School

Untitled

Valentine's is lovely, Valentine's is sweet,
I love Valentine's because I felt the vibration in my feet.
You might find it lovely, or sweet.
You get to send nice pretty cards to who you think is in your dreams,
You might get some cards, or you might not get any.
You might even get a lovely heart pot.
I love my mummy and my daddy, I love everyone in my family
So they are probably very glad,
I love my rabbit, I love my dog and she is called Molly
But . . . I call her Mog.
My mummy got married; she is happy
And, my sister's birds are very flappy;
They play on the swing when the church bell rings
When someone is getting married.
My mummy loves my daddy because they are wife and husband,
And my daddy loves my mummy because they are husband and wife.
I love my two sisters, my nanny and my grandad, as they
are my family,
I love to eat sweets and biscuits, as they are very yummy.
I love doing work for my teachers, they are always happy with me
And I love to read and play my flute,
I love to listen to music and to dance to it at discos,
And I love all the world.

Gaby Pugh (7)
Lakeside Primary School

The Magic Box

(Based on 'Magic Box' by Kit Wright)

I will put in my box . . .
The blinking eye of a worm
Or a fawn coming out of
An egg

I will put in my box . . .
Spring water coming from
A winter night sky
Or a dull rainbow

I will put in my box . . .
The smoothness of the sea
A guitar screeching a tune
Or a spider with one leg

My box is made of . . .
Grains of sand and
Bolted with some ice
From Pluto

I will ride a palomino
Round the corners of my
Fragile box.

Martha Kelsey (8)
Leckhampton Primary School

The Magic Box

(Based on 'Magic Box' by Kit Wright)

I will put in my box . . .
the sound of a book flapping in the breeze,
a turtle speeding at 190 miles per second,
or a rabbit walking on its ears.

I will put in my box . . .
the smell of petrol drifting through a petrol station,
the texture of my bed rippling over my pillow,
or a squirrel pelting nuts at my enemy.

I will put in my box . . .
the taste of chocolate,
the sound of a dead silence sweeping through a deserted, black
world.

My box is made of jelly,
magical duck's feet
and the lock is made of the clearest water.

I will adventure in my box
whisk through the sparkling stars of space
and I will stroll upside down to the end of the universe.

Toby Burden (8)
Leckhampton Primary School

The Magic Box

(Based on 'Magic Box' by Kit Wright)

I will put in my box . . .
A world of darkness,
Rain pouring with money
And the smell of chlorine just put in water.

I will put in my box . . .
Boiling hot snow,
Wells filled with lemonade
Or a worm raving at a party.

In my box I will . . .
Race around on a panda,
Drill forever through the universe,
Or I will live without blinking.

My box is made of . . .
Stones from the moon and
The hinges would be made of
Bolts of lightning from the clouds.

I will put my box in
An attic of a pyramid in
A deserted well.

George Kimpton (9)
Leckhampton Primary School

The Magic Box

(Based on 'Magic Box' by Kit Wright)

I will put in my box . . .
A bright orange snail
Speeding along the racetrack
Or the smell of mouldy old cheese.

I will put in my box . . .
All the annoying sayings of the world,
The best memories ever
And two leap years in a row.

I will put in my box . . .
Fresh warm pizza, made in Antarctica,
The rough feel of sandpaper,
Or a pair of slithering snakes' screams.

My box is made of . . .
The very first tree,
On it are the first stickers invented,
The lock is flimsy for it is made of steel.

I will swim in my box
To the corners of the Earth
Until I end up in paradise.

Sophie Goodrum (9)
Leckhampton Primary School

The Magic Box

(Based on 'Magic Box' by Kit Wright)

I will put in my box . . .
A cheetah going at 1mph,
The smell of freshly mown grass,
Or the sight of a man swimming
With piranhas.

I will put in my box . . .
A cat zooming after a lion,
A little man running round and round in a computer,
Or a different land every day at the top of a tree.

I will put in my box . . .
All the voices in the world,
Or a book reading to itself,
Or maybe a water bottle drinking itself.

My box is made of gold, silver and platinum
With bronze spirals on the top,
With hinges made from ice,
(Not forgetting rubies and emeralds!)

I shall drive into the deepest secrets
In the world.

I keep my box in the most secure
Safe in the universe.

Harry Corder-Gill (8)
Leckhampton Primary School

The Magic Box
(Based on 'Magic Box' by Kit Wright)

I will put in my box . . .
A feeling of a ferret in a yellow dress,
A star made of jelly
Or another world full of trees.

I will put in my box . . .
A sun sprinkling pink rain,
A mouse hunting an eagle
Or a horse full of patterns.

I will put in my box . . .
A boat I can sail in,
A sandwich full of moonbeams
And an oak tree with apples.

My box is made of fur,
I will put wings on it for hinges,
Then I'll sit and talk to
My ferret, mouse and horse.

I will lay stars on the top,
I can fly in my box to the end of the world,
I love diving in my box
And I'll sleep in my box on sheep's wool.

Anna McNeir (8)
Leckhampton Primary School

The Magic Box

(Based on 'Magic Box' by Kit Wright)

I will put in my box . . .
A flying elephant zooming through the street
Or the taste of an orange in my mouth.

I will put in my box . . .
The sea smashing on the rocks
Or a cheetah racing down the street
Or the sound of people talking.

I will put in my box . . .
The tallest tower on Earth
Or a face of a snowman smiling in the snow
Or a lion prancing through the jungle.

My box is made of
Gold and silver
And the hinge is made of bubblegum
With stars on it.

I will fly all night on my magic carpet
Or go to the cold Atlantic ocean.

Katie Smith (8)
Leckhampton Primary School

The Door

(Based on 'The Door' by Miroslav Holub)

Go and open the door
Maybe there are cats of every shape and size
Caterwauling on your garden wall
Or cars hurtling past
Maybe there's a full size oil tanker -
Serenely sailing round your garden pond
Or a wizened old lady walking her pet sofa.

Maybe there are some attractive roses
Which have climbed over your old oak pergola
Or a solitary snowdrop, standing proud
Maybe there's a huge plate of strawberries and cream, put there
                                                    specifically for you
Or an abnormal man with something about him you just can't work out
Go and open the door
At least there'll be a draught.

Catherine Hyde (8)
Leckhampton Primary School

Go And Open The Door

(Based on 'The Door' by Miroslav Holub)

Go and open the door
Maybe there's a cat
Eating a rat
Or a clown with a
Painted face.

Maybe there's
Santa Claus
Or Grandad coming down from Heaven.

Maybe there's a brown parcel with a bright red ribbon
Or a milk bottle with a turquoise lid,
Maybe me swimming with a friend
Or a car flying through space.

Go and open the door
At least there will be a draught.

Charles Glover (8)
Leckhampton Primary School

The Magic Box
(Based on 'Magic Box' by Kit Wright)

I will put in my box . . .
A cat hunting its prey
A tiger afraid of a mouse
And voice of my teacher

I will put in my box . . .
A rubber that won't rub out
A ruler that makes wonky lines
Or the taste of a ripe orange

I will put in my box . . .
The thin lips of a fish
The smell of sweet junk
Or Blu-Tack that doesn't stick

My box is made of
Silver and gold
And has a lock made of Blu-Tack

I shall sunbathe on top of my box
Under the golden sun.

Alice Winter (8)
Leckhampton Primary School

Go And Open The Door

(Based on 'The Door' by Miroslav Holub)

Go and open the door
Maybe there is an interesting
Garden for exploring in
Or there might be a shark
Sliding and being polite

Maybe there are misbehaving
Children
Or the letter C being cool
Down the street

Maybe there are trees falling down
On the floor
Or the H going hyper

Maybe the wind throwing sand
Into people's eyes
Or an elephant stomping down the road

Go and open the door
At least there will be a draught.

Charlotte Buchanan (9)
Leckhampton Primary School

The Magic Box

(Based on 'Magic Box' by Kit Wright)

I will put in my box . . .
The chase of a lioness,
Or the strength of a boxer,
I might even fit in the Statue of Liberty.

I will put in my box . . .
The smell of freshly cut grass
Or the Amazon Rainforest will fit
I'll put in antelope's horns

I will put in my box . . .
A tortoise faster than a Ferrari at full speed
A pack of wolves scared of a baby
Or the coldest ice cream that is minus two hundred
And seventy-one degrees Celsius

My box is made of a living elephant's tummy
The handles are made of pure water straight from the
Amazon Rainforest
The lock is made from salt
And the key is made of air

I keep my box in the darkest corner of the sun
Where it grows up to seventy feet high
But if it gets wet
It will shrink to twenty feet low
When it dries it will start to fly.

Christopher Hope (9)
Leckhampton Primary School

The Door

(Based on 'The Door' by Miroslav Holub)

Go and open the door
Maybe there will be a
City made of chocolate
Or a lamp post shimmering
In the darkness

Maybe there is a desert
Flooded with water
Or just cars zooming
Past my house

Maybe there is a tree
Blowing in the wind
Or children rushing
To school

Go and open the door
At least there will be
A draught.

Bradley Hearn (9)
Leckhampton Primary School

Life's End!

You can't touch it or smell it,
It is cold and bitter,
It takes you when your body starts to decay
By time's evil spell
And when all your years are utterly spent
You surrender your soul to it
It is my greatest fear . . . death!

Rory Birch (11)
Leonard Stanley Primary School

My Dad!

My dad's the kind of dad
Who you really don't want to know,
My friends really disagree
And think he should be on show.

I told them how he really was,
When he's all alone,
I decided to describe him,
So . . .

He's a
Chocolate nicking,
Ear picking,
Bog blocking,
Door locking,
Loud snoring,
Really boring,
Chore delaying,
Hardly paying,
Bad singing,
Hair missing,
Rugby watching,
Never knocking
Dad!

Jodie Atkins (11)
Leonard Stanley Primary School

Peculiar Birth

There once was a boy from Perth,
Who had a peculiar birth;
He popped out of his mummy,
Who had a large tummy
And flew all the way round the Earth!

Calum Murdock (10)
Leonard Stanley Primary School

Post

Sometimes it's good news,
Sometimes it's bad,
It makes people happy,
It makes people sad,
But it definitely comes,
In all shapes and sizes,
Parcels and presents,
They're all surprises!
Letters of thanks,
Letters of joy,
It's a baby girl,
It's a baby boy.
The dreaded bills,
A birthday greeting,
A party invite,
An important meeting.
Sometimes it's good news,
Sometimes it's bad,
It makes people happy,
It makes people sad.

Megan Roberts (11)
Leonard Stanley Primary School

Untitled

There was a man from China
Who wasn't a terrible climber
Whilst fighting with Bill
He fell off a hill
And landed in the hole of a miner.

Luke Murdock (10)
Leonard Stanley Primary School

You Will Find

In the jungle you will find,
Monkeys with an outstanding mind.

In the outback you will see,
A shy koala climbing a tree.

On the cliff top you will spot,
Eagles nesting to keep eggs hot.

You will find on the African plains,
A roaring lion with a tangled mane.

In the desert, burning hot,
Lizards laze beneath a rock.

In the ocean blue and deep,
Sharks swim round, they never sleep.

Lauren Oakes (11)
Leonard Stanley Primary School

Pets

I have a dog called Jess,
That barks all night.
I have a hamster called Charlie,
That eats, all right.
I have a cat called Homer,
That sits on its backside all day.
I have a parrot called Henry,
That chirps all through May.
I have a rabbit called Nibbles,
You can guess why he got his name.
I have a guinea pig called Honey,
Who is always a pain!

Ellen O'Dowd (11)
Leonard Stanley Primary School

My Pets

I have a cat called Cleo,
She has a black coat,
My other pet called Stanley,
Is a mountain goat.

Stanley was very hungry,
So the cat slid down his throat
Naughty mountain goat.

He ran the London marathon,
Thought he'd come first,
But he came last,
Cos he was dying of thirst.

When he arrived home
He flopped onto the mat and died,
Just like that!

Bethany Timbrell (10)
Leonard Stanley Primary School

Fun Day

Blackpool Tower is nice and high
You can see everything in the sky

While I was on the Pepsi Max
My mum was in Halifax

Ironbrew is a good ride
It's a good job my dad sat by my side

Spin Doctor made me dizzy
But the horse ride was not so busy

Now it's time to say goodbye
But my dad told a lie.

Megan Uzzell (9)
Leonard Stanley Primary School

The Big Fat Beast Of The Mountains

Long ago there lived a beast of the mountains,
he had three magical fountains.

He wasn't the slightest bit scary,
but he was very hairy.

He has three eyes
and he always lies.

He has long arms,
plus he likes long walks round farms.

Instead of fire he breathes out water,
did I mention he has a daughter?

She likes to drink from lakes,
she's quite creative but it's the noise she makes.

He has a very fat belly
and the mountain he lives in is very smelly.

When he was young he used to groove,
but now he's old he has to move.

If you see him, quickly look at his face,
because he likes to walk at a pace.

Alex Smith (10)
Leonard Stanley Primary School

Frustration

Don't care about work
In frustration brain overloads
Being annoyed is frustrating
Red-hot anger grows inside
Writing poems is frustrating.

Oliver Harford (10)
Leonard Stanley Primary School

The Cat That Could Not Sleep

There was a cat
As thick as a mat
He went out at night
But had a bit of a fright

He had patches on his ears
Which his owners always fear
He is as clumsy as a bat
And truly he is really fat

One night he could not sleep
Not a wink, not a peep
Tossing, turning all night through
Oh, what was he to do?

His owner came by old and wise
Said, 'Silly cat use your eyes
Can you see that field over there?
It's a field of sheep, try counting them to help you sleep.'

'7, 4, 14, 10, that's not right, I'll try again!'
And then he'd learnt to count the next day!

Nicole Clements (9)
Leonard Stanley Primary School

Alone

Darkness, I just see,
There's no one here beside me,
Down the street I walk,
I'm bitter and in the cold,
Loneliness caught up with me.

Lorna Poultney (10)
Leonard Stanley Primary School

A Pond

A special frog
A soggy log
A little bird
A quiet word

A pond of weed
A mess indeed
A silver fish
A thoughtful wish

A silent snake
A frog to take
A splashing rat
A swimming gnat

A winter night
A frosty bite
A sheet of ice
A nest of mice.

Leanne Harnden (10)
Leonard Stanley Primary School

My Pets

I have a dog called Rocky,
Who likes to jump and play,
I have a budgie called Harry,
Who likes to chirp all day,
I have a rabbit called Shadow,
Who likes to hop around,
I have a guinea pig called Bart,
Who squeaks a loud sound.
I have a guinea pig called Homer,
Who is always lying down,
When I put them together
It makes me very proud.

Danielle Cole (10)
Leonard Stanley Primary School

The Dream Merchant

David was a lazy boy
And his teacher said, 'Oi!
All you do is nod and sleep,
The dream merchant will have to have a peep.'

That night David went to bed
And heard a magical voice in his head,
'I've come to grant you your favourite dream.'
'I want to dream that I'm on a pirate team.'

'What will you pay?'
'I'll pay attention at school the next day.'
Things worked better after that,
He was the best pupil, that's a matter of fact.

Samuel Jones (9)
Leonard Stanley Primary School

My Life

When I was one I sucked my thumb,
When I was two I flushed my dad down the loo,
When I was three I pushed my mum out of the tree,
When I was for I ran into the door,
When I was five I thanked God I was alive,
When I was six I had a giant Twix,
When I was seven I went to Devon,
When I was eight I had a date,
When I was nine I had a fine,
When I was ten, I ate a hen,
When I was old I was going bald,
Now I'm dead, I'm sitting by my mother's side.

Scott Carrington
Leonard Stanley Primary School

My Dog's Life

My dog is liver and white,
He is still a puppy,
Because of this it makes him very, very jumpy,
His antics make me laugh,
Although my shoes do suffer,
Because he chews and chews them so they all go soggy.

My puppy is learning to round up the sheep,
Following his mum,
But every time he goes in the field,
The sheep just run for cover.

Sam Pinker (9)
Leonard Stanley Primary School

Fish On My Hook

Fish in the lake, fish in the sea
Some in ponds, some in tanks
You catch them on your rod
You catch them on your hook

They like sweetcorn, maggots and worms

Scales are golden, scales are grey
Some like pictures, some like space
Mirror carp reflect your face
I love to fish away the day.

Oliver Cooper (10)
Leonard Stanley Primary School

Children Haiku

Children are playing,
All around me I am glad,
I am not alone.

Georgia Matthews (9)
Leonard Stanley Primary School

Poem Problem

I was asked to write a poem of thirty lines or less,
But straight away my head was filled with a boring nothingness.
Shall I write this? Shall I write that?
Shall I write about a monkey or a dog or a cat?
I'll write about a chocolate cake,
No, I'll write about a beautiful blue lake.
Hey - there's a mouse and I've dropped my pen,
Anyway the cat sat - that's useless - I'll start again.
Once upon a fime there lived - no once upon a *time!*
My poem is getting good now - but I've forgot to rhyme!
Okay, I'm really concentrating now,
'Come on write' the teacher says, though really I don't know how.
There are so many things to distract me,
Look out of the window, is that a plane I see?
(Must focus) what rhymes with door?
Hmmm, I've got it, floor!
I've only done a line so far
And it's so noisy in here, the door is still ajar.
I'll have to write and write and write,
Else I'll be here all night!
I'm down to the last verse now,
My arm aches really badly, *ow!*
Only fifty-four words left to do,
Everyone says it was too hard, too true.
The last word, what shall it be?
Something that will miraculously finish me . . .
At last I'm done put down my pen,
But I hear a voice say, 'That's not good enough
Start again!'

Ella Harriss (10)
Leonard Stanley Primary School

Desert Haiku

Hot, red sun beats down,
Pyramids stand all alone,
Sun blazing on them.

Ford Sass (8)
Leonard Stanley Primary School

Trees Haiku

Talking together,
Groaning through the damp woodland,
Why do we chop them?

Prudence Morgan-Wood (9)
Leonard Stanley Primary School

Rainforests Haiku

Tall, green canopy,
No light shining through the trees,
Leaves cover the sky.

William Richardson (8)
Leonard Stanley Primary School

Tiger Haiku

Prowling through the trees,
Waiting to pounce on its prey,
Hoping for its lunch.

Ben Sztanko (8)
Leonard Stanley Primary School

Unknown Bloke

The wind was like a hurricane,
Ripping up the grass,
The moon was like a lantern,
Lighting up the path,
Then through the darkened wood
Came a dark figure in a big black hood,
The hood happened to be part of a cloak,
Wrapped around the unknown bloke,
The bloke's horse looked tired but able,
He led his horse into the stable,
Then the bloke himself came into the inn,
He gave his name and asked for a gin,
He paid the innkeeper enough to stay a night,
Because the night gave him a bit of a fright.

Mackenzie Young (9)
Nailsworth CE Primary School

You

Your blonde hair shines,
Shines over your scarlet coat,
Your ice-blue eyes sparkle,
Sparkle in the golden sun.
You move silently,
More silently than a mouse,
Your scarlet coat glimmers,
Glimmers in the noon sun.
Your smile brightens,
Brightens all that's dark,
Your laugh breaks,
Breaks all that's silent,
Your nature puts,
Puts a smile on everyone's dull face.

Jacob Chew (10)
Nailsworth CE Primary School

The Pony

The pony gallops and runs
Like a gust of wind
On a cold winter's night

The pony's fluttering mane
Frantically waves
On a cold winter's night

The pony's hooves clatter
In the moonlight as the moon fades away
On a cold winter's night

The pony's dazzling body shines
In the moonlight
On a cold winter's night

Trot, trot
Trot
Trot, trot.

Hannah Ravenhill (10)
Nailsworth CE Primary School

Death Round Every Corner

This poem starts at the heart
In no more than a lane
A little girl waits, she waits, a dark shadow
Glides, it glides. The girl runs, a cackle, laugh
From a corner. The girl's mind whizzes. A harsh
Wind blew. This cannot say anymore about who, what or
Why this shadow was, it's just her last breathe of the world.
This is how she felt, she screamed, she fell, she
Muttered. Then she was *gone*. Her last words were . . .

Izzy Davis (10)
Nailsworth CE Primary School

My Dog

My dog wakes up,
Has Weetabix,
Goes into the sitting room
Looks at the chairs,
Barks at the door to try and get out.
I let her go into the garden.
When she is outside she barks for about 20 minutes,
Smells the flowers,
Goes back inside,
Goes into the kitchen,
Goes to her basket and sleeps.

Henry Watts (9)
Nailsworth CE Primary School

Animals In The Jungle

In the jungle the lion lives with his big yellow mane
And sharp white teeth

In the jungle the monkey lives with his fuzzy brown hair
And his cheeky little smile

In the jungle the snake lives with his slithery green scales
And his beady black eyes

In the jungle the tiger lives with his stripy orange body
And his big white paws

In the jungle the spider lives with his eight hairy legs
And his silky, shiny web.

Rebecca Long (10)
Nailsworth CE Primary School

Tigger The Tabby Cat

Monday: Tigger eats, drinks and sleeps
Tuesday: Tigger eats, drinks, scratches and sleeps
Wednesday: Tigger eats, drinks, scratches, digs and sleeps
Thursday: Tigger eats, drinks, scratches, digs, makes love and sleeps
Friday: Tigger eats, drinks, scratches, digs, makes love,
hogs the fire and sleeps
Saturday: Tigger eats, drinks, scratches, digs, makes love,
hogs the fire, chases a mouse and sleeps
Sunday: Tigger eats, drinks, scratches, digs, makes love,
hogs the fire, chases a mouse, washes and sleeps.

Katie Gay (9)
Nailsworth CE Primary School

The Day In The Life Of Ron The Budgie

Ron flutters frantically and chirps around the room
If he poops, uh-oh my mum is in doom!
My bird is a bit of a poser
With my camera I can go closer and closer!
I love my budgie oh so very dear
Uh-oh I think I'm gonna shed a tear!

Chloe Marsden (10)
Nailsworth CE Primary School

Bell, The Dog

Bell wakes up, eats, goes into the garden
Barks at some birds as loud as a foghorn,
Finds a shady place behind a greenhouse,
Comes back in and sleeps.
Bell wakes up, runs into the lounge
Then into the kitchen,
Eats and sleeps.

Simon Amos (9)
Nailsworth CE Primary School

The World Is As Lonely As The Blue Sky

The world is as lonely as the blue sky
As lonely as a bird crashing and dying
In the twirling vanilla sky
As the sun set
My back hurts and so does my thigh
The peacefulness breaks
The quietness breaks as it dies
As the sun sets, as I die
I hope this world is a better place to lie.

Mustafijur Rohman (10)
Nailsworth CE Primary School

If I Only Had One Wish

If I only had one wish
I'd plant it in a cloud
And watch the rain pour it down
So people can see
The sunshine spread

If I only had one wish
I'd throw it into space
For the astronauts
To see and feel the happiness
For them spread around the Earth

If I had only one wish
I'd break it in bits
And throw it through
Open windows
For everyone to feel

If I had only one wish
I'd let it go
Floating through the Earth
And see the hope
Spread through people's hearts.

Gaby Chilton (10)
Northleach CE Primary School

If I Had Only One Wish

If I had only one wish
I'd throw it in the ocean
And watch it float away
To travel across the world
And help everyone across the nation

If I had only one wish
I'd throw it in the lake
And I'd watch it ripple
As it got bigger and bigger
Like love on the world

If I had only one wish
I'd throw it in the glowing fire
And see the warmth inside hour by hour
As it glistens in the happy world
Rejoicing in song.

Kirstie Smith (11)
Northleach CE Primary School

Let Us

Let us have peace and love at Christmas
Not have killing or dying

Let us be with our family at Christmas
Not in a trench

Let us joke and have fun together
Not let death part us

Let us stay with our friends
Not with strangers

Let us sing together
Not argue with each other.

Bethany Collado (10)
Northleach CE Primary School

My Miracle

If I had only one wish
I'd throw it in the snow
And watch it camouflage with the
White powder and affect the
Warmness of the world

If I had only one miracle
I'd drop it onto the Earth
And stand astonished as it brings
And makes a path for everyone
Across the universe

If I had only one desire
I'd print it on a board
And feel the joy of
My friends that the
Heart-beating landscape has given.

Laura See (10)
Northleach CE Primary School

Let Us Feel Love In Our Hearts

Let us fall in laughter together,
Not descend to death.

Let us put our differences aside,
Not pull triggers of death.

Let us see merry men,
Not the ghosts arising.

Let us eat a four course meal,
Not the nature of Earth.

Let our souls fill with light,
Not the darkness of Hell.

Let us feel love in our hearts,
Not the bullets of pain.

Thomas Williams (10)
Northleach CE Primary School

If I Had Only One Wish

If I had only one wish
I would throw it into the fire
And look at the flame growing
Higher and higher
Building onto the coal

If I had only one wish
I would see it sprinkle
Down to Earth
And see the puddles
Splash and splash

If I had only one wish
I would say something for it to echo
As it answers back
Replying its name
Back to Earth

If I had only one wish
I would bury it in soil
And see it inch by inch
Grow with the power
Of a living thing in this silent world.

Hannah Creed (11)
Northleach CE Primary School

A Poppy Reminds Me

A poppy reminds me of peace and love
Of all the people safe above

All of the poppies blowing around
Motionless bodies led on the ground

The red of a poppy is so red
Is it because of the decaying dead?

They fought for our country so we could be free
And to carry the remembrance is up to you and me.

Aiden Bassett (11)
Northleach CE Primary School

If I Had Only One Wish

If I had only one wish
I'd throw it into the sea
And watch it spread
Into the world to give
Joy and happiness

If I had only one wish
I'd bury it deep into the ground
And feel it spread warmth and
Joy into the
Cold world

If I had only one wish
I'd put it in a tree
And watch every
Face crack into
One huge grin of happiness.

Ashleigh Rudd (11)
Northleach CE Primary School

Let Us Form A Truce

Let us drink beer,
Not the dew of death.

Let us fill our stomachs with food,
Not fill them with emptiness.

Let us hear the sounds of Christmas carols,
Not the screams of death.

Let us fight for our country,
Not for death and glory.

Let us share and give,
Not take and lie.

Let us form a truce for as long as we can.

Richard Tapsell (11)
Northleach CE Primary School

War

Let us play with them,
Not play with guns of death.

Let us drink to a truce,
Not drink the blood of others.

Let us sing to silence,
Not fear of war.

Let us give to others,
Not give dead bodies.

Let us speak together and laugh,
Not laugh at the dead bodies in no-man's-land.

Let us say Merry Christmas,
Not scream out loud with pain.

Let us stop the endless war,
Not let it remain.

Let us win the football match,
Not win the war.

Let us stay on Earth for another day,
Not go to Heaven now.

Let us hug our family for real,
Not dream we would.

Let us ring out word 'Peace',
Not the word 'War'.

Ellen Wilkins (10)
Northleach CE Primary School

If I Had Only One Wish

If I had only one wish
I'd give everyone a
Teddy and see
Their faces glow and
Brighten up everywhere

If I had only one wish
I would let everyone
Do everything they want
And help people do
The things they can't do

If I had only one wish
I would give everyone
A pet to play with
And food to give them
And see the kindness within

If I had only one wish
I'd give everyone a
Miracle to use so
I can see the happiness
Around the world.

Chris Mills (10)
Northleach CE Primary School

It Was So Still

It was so calm that I felt
My heart beating
Frantically . . .

It was so silent that I heard
The lights nattering
Like old women . . .

It was so quiet that I heard
My earrings screaming
When I turned them . . .

It was so silent that I heard
The dictionaries saying
'My head hurts . . .'

It was so still that I saw
A cold, grey statue
Open its eyes and smile.

Rosie Leach (10)
Northleach CE Primary School

Peace And War

Let us sing and dance,
Not fight and quarrel.

Let us put the Christmas tree up,
Not knock it down.

Let us share food and beer,
Not anger and hatred.

Let us call it a truce,
Not keep on killing.

Michael Kent (10)
Northleach CE Primary School

If I Had Only One Wish

If I had only one wish
I would gear it into a clock
And bring Jesus back
To shine in the
Darkness of the world

If I had only one wish
I would build a bridge
Of hope to those who have
None to be a beacon of
Hope for the world

If I had only one wish
I would catapult it into the sky
And watch the flittering glitter of love
Spreading over the world
And dissolving all hatred and evil.

Henry Fothergill (11)
Northleach CE Primary School

The Silence

You hear the silence,
The flags are raised,
In memory of the men that died that day,
Then the soft, smooth sound of the trumpet that plays,
The men that fought and survived,
With their medals shining in the golden sun,
Saluting to their many friends in the blue sky,
Then numerous people put poppies on the war memorial,
We are grateful to these men,
We give thanks to these men,
Because we live in peace.

Jo Drinkwater (10)
Northleach CE Primary School

Lauren Rose Shine

Lauren Rose is forty,
She's always lived alone,
She will eat what gets in her way,
She does nothing but moan.

Her clothes are ripped and dirty,
Her toenails have never been cut,
She lives with the high brown trees,
Whose door is always shut.

Too scared to go to sleep,
She would only sit and stare,
She wondered what would happen,
No one would ever care.

She would always be very upset,
She would just sit and sew,
No one would dare visit her gravestone,
She died many years ago.

Chloe Phillips (9)
Parkend Primary School

I Am Me!

I am not a kangaroo
I am not a giraffe
I am not a zebra
I am not an elephant
I am not a tiger
I am not a crocodile
I am not a pig
I am not a monkey
I am not a lion
I am not a camel
I am me!

George Stratford (7)
Parkend Primary School

Chuk Chuk Chukie

Chukie lived in a tree house
Which was in the eerie, dark wood
His friends were the trees and grass
And all alone he stood

He went for a jolly walk
He met a jumpy Josh
They spent their time picking apples
And drinking scrumptious squash

Now this is what Josh is like
He is often in the town
He has blue hair and a big nose
He always has a frown

Chukie went back to his tree house
Waving Josh goodbye
Chukie was becoming very ill
So off he went to die.

Claire Preest (9)
Parkend Primary School

I Am Me

I am not a fish
I am me
I am not a dragon
I am me
I am not an elephant
I am me!

Laura Taylor (5)
Parkend Primary School

The Ghost Knight

Michael is a brave young knight
He roams around the dark wood
His wife Anne is a pretty sight
He wears a rare blue hood
He has dark-coloured chain-mail
He rides a strong white horse
He charges off, rides into battle
He is very tough of course
He eats raw meat and bat's blood
And plum juice sour as lemons
He feasts upon the floor of tiles
And likes vicious beasts and demons
He won't rest until he gets revenge
He lurks around every door
He lurks around every tower
Four years later he lives no more.

Rhees Davis (11)
Parkend Primary School

I Am Me

I am me
I am not a dinosaur
I am not a dragon
I am not a duck
I am not an eagle
I am not a lion
I am me!

Craig Hinchliffe (6)
Parkend Primary School

Cinderella And The Tomato Soup

One day when Cinders was alone,
She cleaned and cleaned then found a phone,
She picked it up but was unsure,
But in a flick 'knock' went the door,
Cinders went outside then found,
Lying in front of her on the ground,
A metal can of tomato soup,
She opened it with a big loud *whoop!*

Cinders drank it down in one,
Then had a feeling of funky fun,
Her rags turned into a bright ballgown,
She no longer looked like a stupid clown,
She thought, *good riddance to a mucky life,*
I'm not gonna be your housewife.
The prince then arrived in a silver coach,
'My wife has left with my golden brooch.

So off Cinders went to a local mall
And then she sold the brooch at a market stall,
Cinders then lived a happy life,
But still she was the prince's wife.

Lara Shingles (10)
Parkend Primary School

Fun At Playtime Is . . .

Hiding, seeking
Football, tag
Snakes, ladders
Skipping, running
I like it.

Joe Thomas (6)
Parkend Primary School

Joey Xatua

Joey Xatua is as rich as can be,
He owns a massive mall shop
And has enough money to buy the world,
He sells a lot of pop.

Joey wears expensive clothes,
Of black, white and beige,
Long coat, baggy jeans, skater top and shoes,
They all suit his very young age.

The food he eats, is very tasty,
From vegetables to caviar and wine,
His drinks, every time it's sweet,
From Coke to anything he can find.

His age is only twenty,
Always a vacant expression,
Happy, he's never heard of it,
You'd think he had a profession.

Nice Joey, he was a fair man,
Voted king of the world today,
He was a master duellist, but died doing so,
His death, so tragic, it was the 1st of May.

Thomas Hodder (11)
Parkend Primary School

The Animals

The animals that I drew
Would like to show us what they can do
The duck can quack and fly in the sky
The giraffe can eat the leaves up high
The seal can clap and play with a ball
I think that my animals are really cool.

Liam Sheppard (7)
Parkend Primary School

Jolly Joanne

Joanne she works in an office,
Answering the red phone
She was always very joyful
You never hear her groan

Her face is as fresh as apples
She was sixty years old
Joanne kept herself looking smart
By always wearing gold

Her favourite meal is roast
Her pudding is jelly
She likes to eat every yummy food
She has a big belly

Joanne became a granny
She had a grandson who was brave
Poor Joanne became very ill
Then went to her grave.

Hannah O'Connell (10)
Parkend Primary School

Why?

'Where are you going?'
'To the pub.'
'Why?'
'Because I want to go out for a drink.'
'Why?'
'Because I like it.'
'Why?'
'Because I'm thirsty.'
'Why?'
'Why don't you stop saying why?'
'What?'

Eleanor Brown (5)
Parkend Primary School

Goldilocks

There once were three bears,
Who were covered in hairs,
They preferred cold porridge to hot,
So one fine day,
They went away
And returned with a baby's cot,
But while they were away,
A girl came to play,
Although she did not do that a lot,
She wasn't very nice,
She killed all their mice
And broke young Baby Bear's pot,
There up ahead
She was led,
In young little Baby Bear's cot,
She woke up with fear
And ran to a near
Window without a lock,
Goldilocks was never seen
Again by the bear who was very pleased,
So no more porridge eaten by
A girl's life which is a lie.

Chelsea Turley (10)
Parkend Primary School

I Am Me

I am me,
I am not a frog,
I am me, not a crocodile,
I am me, not a duck,
I am me, not a bird,
I am not, not a snake,
I am me.

Hollie Seaborn (6)
Parkend Primary School

Dirty Joe

Dirty Joe ate scraps from bins
He's like a rat on the street
Once a famous football player
He begs at people's feet

He lives in a dirty barn
Eating scraps from a bin
Gets leftovers from old take-aways
He was so very thin

An old raincoat he would wear
He wore old smelly socks
He smelt like a street rat
He made his shoes out of a box

Joe looks like an ugly pig
He looks like a grubby horse . . .
A muddy puddle on a winter's day
His best meal is tomato sauce.

Stuart Jones (9)
Parkend Primary School

Grumpy Old Joey

Joey is a begging, grumpy man,
He has no friends at all,
He lives in a small dustbin bag,
Everything he has is small.

They call him Lonely Old Joe,
You never hear him sing,
No one ever comes to visit,
Or gives him a friendly ring.

His bag has a great big hole,
His clothes all dark and tight,
He eats dead rats for supper,
Before he says goodnight.

Kerri Davis (10)
Parkend Primary School

Old Captain Jack Sparrow

There was an old pirate ghost ship
That had lots of pirate gold
The captain was named Jack Sparrow
He was covered in ugly mould

There was a big, raging, black storm
That wanted to have a fight
It started to build up its big waves
And flung them with all its might

The old captain Jack Sparrow
Wore a very big, scary hat
It hung down over his freaky face
The same as his furry cat

The food that he ate was sick
It was human legs and bone
All the crew liked razor fish stew
The smell made Captain Jack moan.

Jed Leach (11)
Parkend Primary School

Kaiba

Kaiba is a teenager
He likes to play a card game
He likes to show off day and night
Some people are pretty lame

Kaiba is in deep danger
He tripped in a pile of mud
Then he woke up in the street
Everyone thought he was a stud

He loves to ride his skateboard
Sometimes he feels quite cool
People reckon he's a pro
Although he acts like a fool.

Jack Brace (10)
Parkend Primary School

Grubby Joe

Grubby Joe lives like a rat,
Inside a mouldy box,
On the street begging for money,
With his dirty old socks.

All he can eat are leftovers,
From a greasy old bin,
As lonely as a dry desert,
His best meal is in a tin.

He has a ripped, rotten cloak,
The same clothes he always wears,
His trousers are tied with grubby string,
But at least he is not bare.

He lived in the dark, alone,
Like a bag of cold coal,
He's the loneliest man ever,
Like a cold, cold, blind mole.

Matthew Powell (10)
Parkend Primary School

Mario

Mario is trapped in the wood
He would escape if he could
The trees are singing in the wood
The wood is crunching
By the field the mud is squelchy
By the wood Mario is frightened
Because the owls are singing their favourite song
The flood is squelchy
Belsor's guards are asleep for good.

Jake Fletcher (8)
Parkend Primary School

Kangaroo Hunt

One dark night near Ayres Rock in Australia
A baby kangaroo lost all alone in the dark
Small but sad, he apprehensively hopped and bounced
And stopped, sniffed the night's blowing air
Scared, shivering like he was in a block of ice

He sniffed and started to hop again,
He wanted to find his mum,
Night was ending, sun arising, morning awoke,
He saw some kangaroos passing by,
Hundreds, even thousands, miscellaneous numbers,
He saw his mum, he hopped and hopped,
He was so excited he joined them all.

Henry Jones (9)
Parkend Primary School

Football World Poem

Beckham bends the ball,
Heskey headers high balls,
Ljungberg limps to the leather,
Okacha opens against Owen,
Adriano is aggressive to Alexandro,
Doif dies for Djemba-Djemba,
Foe fights for Ferdinand,
Redknapp races for Ronaldo.

Brazil bites for Botswana,
Sweden shine so seriously,
Australia are aggressive to Austria,
Denmark donate to the Dominican Republic,
England excuse Edinburgh.

Joseph Aldridge (9)
Parkend Primary School

All Fall Down

A squirrel it came to me
It made a dent on my window sill
It dashed, it crashed

A sight that met my eyes, it was a tiger
It pounced on my window sill
The window sill cracked again
The tiny tiger ran into the woods

I saw a tall giraffe
It galloped on my window sill
Half of my window sill fell off
And so did the giraffe
Then I started to cry

I saw an elephant, he was very shy
He jumped on my window sill
My house toppled over!

Rowan Uzzell (9)
Parkend Primary School

A Trap In The Woods

Once I went into the woods to plant my beanstalk
The woods were so quiet I didn't want to talk
I took a big step and fell into a trap
And I said, 'Where am I? I wish I had a map.'
Then I dropped my seed and it only made a little tap,
Then the beanstalk grew and lifted me out of the trap.
I looked down and found out that it was a trap,
I thought I didn't really need a map,
I looked behind myself and saw my beanstalk,
Then I walked home and didn't forget how to talk!

Ross James (7)
Parkend Primary SchoolG

Animals

In Mount Rushmoor there is a deep, dark forest, there are . . .
Leaping lions that like licking lemmings
Five ferocious foxes feeding on ferrets
Pouncing parked panthers like peanuts
Two trampling tiny tigers touch their tummies twice
Clever cats clinging cleverly on cups
Four freezing pheasants fought for freedom
Lazy leopards like linen
Eight enormous elephants eat Ecuador energetically.

Alex Brown (9)
Parkend Primary School

Sea Life

One obedient octopus obeys others
Two tiny turtles tickle their toes
Three thick fishes think
Four flat fishes flash their fins
Five flying fishes flashed like flames
Six skinny sharks sang sweetly
Seven smelly sea lions sail silently
Eight elegant eagles eat
Nine nasty narwhals need to be naughty
Ten tiny tunas tidy their toys.

Ella Warsop (8)
Parkend Primary School

Football Not Netball

I saw a football not a netball
It went in a goal not a net
They used their feet not their hands
They had leather balls not bouncy plastic balls.

Matthew Aldridge (9)
Parkend Primary School

I Went Into A Submarine

I went into a submarine I saw . . .
An obscure octopus impaling other fish
A stupid shark bashing into wrecked ships
A fearsome shoal of flaming fish
A frightened furious family of flat fish
A tornado of troublesome turtles
A stupendous swordfish chasing his prey
That's what I saw when I went in a submarine.

Benjamin Stratford (9)
Parkend Primary School

The Rainforest

Once there lived a parrot, parrot, parrot,
Once there lived a tiger, tiger, tiger,
Once there lived a hippo, hippo, hippo,
Once there lived a lion, lion, lion,
Once there lived a gorilla, gorilla, gorilla,
Once there lived a shark, shark, shark,
The sharks came towards the animals . . .
And ate them all up and only one lived!

Stuart Clarke (7)
Parkend Primary School

Fighting Firemen

Firemen jumping into the truck
They can't wait to put out that fire
Driving through the town
With the blue light glowing
Climbing up the ladder
To rescue the people
To retire with money.

Emily Worgan (9)
Parkend Primary School

A Storm At Sea

Big waves crashing
Bright lightning flashing
Noisy thunder bashing

Wooden boats swinging
Wet arm flinging
Icy, choppy sea
Misty fog as sparkly as water

Flashing lighthouse beaming
Scary ghosts singing
Noisy people screaming
Scattering mice squeaking
Small rats eating.

Savanna Tyler (9)
Parkend Primary School

The Underground Research Base

I was underground,
I didn't know where I was,
I looked at my map,
My rucksack was fat,
There was a zombie I killed,
I wish I had gills because soon I had to swim,
I pounced and hung onto a bar,
I leapt off the bar into the water and swam,
I got out of the water,
I electrocuted a zombie so basically I murdered,
Or if you like, tortured, then I raced out.

Otto Linden (7)
Parkend Primary School

The Five Days Of Christmas

On the first day of Christmas my barman sold to me
A lager for 17p
On the second day of Christmas my barman sold to me
A dotted cocktail with a cherry on the top and a lager for 17p
On the third day of Christmas my barman sold to me
Some old teabag papers, a dotted cocktail with a cherry on the top
and a lager for 17p
On the fourth day of Christmas my barman offered me
The great big bar stool, an old piece of teabag paper, a dotted
cocktail with a cherry on the top and a lager for 17p
On the fifth day of Christmas my barman offered me
A big bag of peanuts, the great big bar stool, an old piece of teabag
paper, a dotted cocktail with a cherry on the top and a lager for 17p!

Jack Turley (8)
Parkend Primary School

Mr Frank Box

There was a big, big mansion
On top of a dark hill,
Where Mr Frank Box, a creepy old man
Sat on the small window sill.

He wore a grey and black hat
And a brown and green cloak,
His trousers all grim, his shirt shred,
Enough to make you choke.

He ate things from the grim tip,
Like rotten old apples,
He digs in the chip shop bins,
He goes to the local chapel.

Alasdair Hinchliffe (10)
Parkend Primary School

Listen, What Can You Hear?

Listen, what can you hear?
Cat running down the hall, bats and rats
Running up the wall
Listen, what can you hear?
Dogs and frogs and misty fogs
Listen, what can you hear?
Birds singing, doorbells ringing, Mr Sleemun singing.

Listen.

Alex Hooper (8)
Parkend Primary School

Bugs And Creatures

Beetles stomping in the wood
Ants clomping angrily
Grasshoppers jumping quickly
Bees buzzing around
Wasps stinging badly
Earwigs crawling anxiously
Butterflies fluttering swiftly
Moths flying friendly
Ladybirds walking softly.

Faye Lewis (9)
Parkend Primary School

The Forest Of Ghost

In a ghost haunted forest
In ancient castles,
Cobwebbed and windy,
Every hour a screaming
Sound comes from the dungeons
And a red watch tower
And watch out for the power
And watch out for the human hunters . . .

Dan Pope (9)
Parkend Primary School

I'm Just Going Out

'I'm just going out for a moment.'
'Why?'
'Because we have no food.'
'Why?'
'Because you have eaten it all.'
'Why?'
'Because you are always hungry.
Why don't you stop saying why?'
'Why?'
'Stop saying why!'
'What?'

Lauren Roberts (7)
Parkend Primary School

Tractors

John Deere, County, Massey, Case
About to start a ploughing race
International, Fergie, Valmet, Ford
Too many to watch! You'll never be bored!

Vintage and modern ploughing around
It's amazing to see furrows in the ground
It's beginning to rain and some are getting stuck
What a pity! What bad luck!

The day's nearly over, ploughing done
I really had such good fun!
The Zetor's going up by the hill
Case going by the mill

Massey towing the big trailer
Here comes a Ford with an old, round baler
County going up for a run
There's a mini digger having some fun.

Jason Roberts (11)
St Anthony's Convent School, Cinderford

Mog, Bog And Clog

Bog is black with little white spots,
With a little blue collar with a golden dot.
He likes to play with horses as they trot,
Over the fields with crops that rot.
Some people think that he's a clot.

Mog is gold with a little white paw,
Her family are quite poor,
So when she is hungry, she doesn't get anymore,
She wears a pink ribbon that makes her proud
And everyone says she stands out in a crowd.

Clog is a dog that is bright,
He can almost fly a kite.
If it's a good flight,
He can fly it with all his might.

Katherine MacLean (11)
St Anthony's Convent School, Cinderford

If

If I was a doctor and used needles
Which are sharp and which shine
And I dipped wounds in brine
I'd get to deal with people who had had too much wine
And I'd get to see people who weren't feeling fine

If I was a traveller and went to sunny beaches
I could sit down and eat peaches
Or I could go to places which are cold
Where it is impossible for food to mould

If I worked at the vet's
And saw people with their pets
Sometimes they'd get infections
So I'd have to give injections.

Thomas Tremlett (10)
St Anthony's Convent School, Cinderford

My Father

My father, what a humble man
Has been going strong for as long as he can
He is not lazy, not a bit
For all of those years spent down the pit
Dawn till dusk on his hands and knees
Didn't even pay for all of his needs
Twelve bricks on each shoulder carrying the hod
Made him sweat buckets but he still carried on
As time went by things began to change
The better the job, the more money he gained
His next job was Westbury Homes
This hardworking man would never moan
I am proud of my father, for all that he has done
I hope I can grow up to be his ideal son.

Daniel Bell (10)
St Anthony's Convent School, Cinderford

The Big Red Armchair

I'm everyone's favourite chair,
Shame really I wasn't a pair,
Lived in the same house for fifty years,
I have big red wings that look like ears,
My legs are wooden, round and thick,
My arms are padded like a brick,
My cushions are sagging, springs poke through,
No more jobs for me to do,
In the corner is my place,
With a window by me in red and white lace,
Today I've been dumped in a skip,
Tomorrow I'll will be taken to the tip.

Sophie Linton (10)
St Anthony's Convent School, Cinderford

Tractors

That tractor is a John Deere,
I don't think he has got the right gear,
He's going up a hill,
To the busy sawmill.

When you are driving a Ford,
You never get bored.
If you are towing a trailer,
It is different from towing a baler.

Everyone's favourite was a little grey Fergi,
It was built to last, strong and sturdy
And then there was the David Brown,
So sparkly and clean, you could drive it into town!

Manituo is French,
It could lift up a bench,
The tractor made by Zetor,
Is definitely not a cheater.

Ben Stephens (11)
St Anthony's Convent School, Cinderford

The Cat

Once upon a time,
I decided to write a rhyme,
I wrote about a cat,
His name was Billy Bat,
He runs all around
And over the grassy ground.
He likes to chase his tail,
When it's blown in the gale.
He wanders in the dark
And he definitely doesn't bark.
He's usually at his best
And likes to make a nest
And guess by whom he's owned?
Well, he lives on his own!

James Hamell (10)
St Anthony's Convent School, Cinderford

My Family

My mum bought a car
It doesn't go very far
The AA van brought it back
Then my mum gave it a good old whack

My sister's got curly hair
She is not always fair
She can be very quiet
But can also run a riot

My dad is an engineer
He travels far and near
He likes to play football with me
I trip him up and kick him in the knee

We have four cats, Cleo, Peach, Basil and Bart,
Of our family they are a real part,
Snoring and purring and washing all day
And sometimes they have the energy to play.

Finally there's me, there's not much to tell,
My name is Callum, my mum calls me Cal,
Sometimes my dad says I lose the plot,
Must be going! That's the lot!

Callum Ireland (10)
St Anthony's Convent School, Cinderford

A Bad Fairy

You would think that all fairies are nice,
But this one gives you such a fright,
You think she's going round the bend
And she doesn't have a single friend.

She is round, fat and witty
And people think she's pretty,
But when you know the real her,
You don't know what will occur.

She's always sneaking about at night,
Giving everyone a fright,
Turning you into frogs and rats
And maybe slugs, mice or bats.

Where she lives is quite scary,
The people there are round, fat and hairy,
But if you ever go near there,
Please watch out and do
Beware!

Christina O'Carroll (11)
St Anthony's Convent School, Cinderford

Black And White

Lost in a world, black and white,
People flying out of sight,
Gargoyles gurgling under bridges,
Dragons sitting on snow-capped ridges,
Wolves howling to the stars,
No civilisation or cars.

No part of this place is ever bright,
The sky does not shed any light,
Gnomes grabbing at your legs,
Eagles eating buried eggs,
No one sings, no pretty things.

Does anyone have a happy face?
I really truly hate this place,
The trees are shrinking to the ground,
My head is spinning round and round
And nobody cares at all, at all,
And nobody cares at all.

Chloe Walding (10)
St Anthony's Convent School, Cinderford

Bonnie

My dog, Bonnie, is a wonderful dog
She would play all day in rain
Outside she would go with her chewy toy
She is never ever a pain

While Bonnie was outside
She looked up and saw a cat!
Then she jumped up and down
By where the cat was sat

When she comes in she finds somewhere to sit
Somewhere warm to dry off her fur
Then when she is nice and dry
I would go and cuddle up to her

That is a poem about my dog
Though she is only three
She also is quite little
I'm sure that she loves me.

Oliver Fitt (11)
St Anthony's Convent School, Cinderford

Big Nose Bob

Big Nose Bob
Is a slob!
He has a red nose,
It really glows!
He has a big beard,
It makes him look weird!
He has a Mercedes-Benz,
But has no friends.
His laughter's a bit wearing,
But his nature is always caring.
He has knobbly toes,
Lined up in rows.
He picks his nose
And wipes it down his clothes.
He wears a brown vest,
To cover his hairy chest
And last but not least,
He loves to have feasts!

Jessica Mason (10)
St Anthony's Convent School, Cinderford

Changing Seasons

Gentle showers, watery sun,
Flowers peep from the cold soil,
Lambs jump, skip and run,
Mothers watch and continue their toil.

Summer heat, beaches blaze,
Bathers show their bodies white,
Yachts float in the misty haze,
Barbecues held into the night.

Autumn colours here at last,
Golden, orange, brown and red,
I love to walk and kick the leaves, but,
It's a shame everything is dead.

Cold winds, bright white snow,
Playing, rolling, building high,
Glad we've not got far to go,
Stars shine in the clear night sky.

Seasons come and seasons go,
Changing, ever changing then,
Each time one disappears,
The next comes round in turn again.

Karl Turner (11)
St Anthony's Convent School, Cinderford

Friends

Chloe is funny and she is cool,
Ollie likes to kick around a ball,
Jess is smart and crazy at times,
Jason likes his chocolate especially Dimes,
Claire is giggly and always kind,
Karl is a bit of a mastermind,
Sophie likes to laugh and play,
Ben is happy all the day,
Poppy is a football fan,
Danny is going to be a big man,
Christina is good at sport,
Katherine is a good sort,
Josh is good as art,
Thomas likes a jam tart,
James wears glasses
And every exam Callum passes.

Holly Smith (10)
St Anthony's Convent School, Cinderford

My Little Brother

My little brother is such a menace,
He's very loud, just like me.
He's very playful, just like me.
He chatters a lot, just like me.
He laughs a lot, just like me.
He runs around, just like me.
He makes a mess, just like me,
But he's my brother . . .
I love him and he loves me.

Gwennan Williams (8)
St David's Primary School, Moreton-in-Marsh

World War II Poem

Young men fought to keep us free
They used guns, ships, aircraft, tanks,
Bombs, torpedoes and bayonets,
They fought Germany, Japan and Italy,
On both sides, many survived but many died.

The English felt sorry for the French,
Because some were children, as well as grown-ups,
Who were killed by the Germans,
They were *bad, bad, bad!*

Sometimes children as young as two days old
Were killed and animals too,
This was *sad, sad, sad.*

This was over 60 years ago
And we all should not forget
Our young men, each of them is a hero
To keep us free, we will never forget
What they did for us.

Catriona Wilcox (8)
St David's Primary School, Moreton-in-Marsh

Justin Timberlake

Justin Timberlake is my hero
Cameron is a total zero
If I was him, I'd marry me
Maybe sometime he will see
The lady I will *be!*

Justin Timberlake is my hero
Cameron is a total zero
We will be the first in line
Then we will have a smashing time
And I'll be his señorita.

Lucy Jasinski (11)
St David's Primary School, Moreton-in-Marsh

Unique

You are different in every way,
Whatever you think, whatever you say,
Whether your eyes are blue or smoky-grey,
You're certainly unique.

A ginger curl,
A highlights girl,
Streaks of pearl,
You're certainly unique.

Tall and burly,
Moody and surly,
Pink and girly,
You're certainly unique.

Well, what really can I say,
To end this magic rhyme today?
There only is a single way;
You're certainly unique.

Daisy Lindlar (11)
St David's Primary School, Moreton-in-Marsh

Rainforest

Rainforest, rainforest
I'm calling to you
Will you give me the sound of a blue cockatoo?

Rainforest, rainforest
Mountains may guard you
But when I am captain they will be crew

Rainforest, rainforest,
Fast asleep
I will wait in the mist to hear the animals meet.

Rhiannon Davies (10)
St David's Primary School, Moreton-in-Marsh

At The Beach

Shell collecting,
Sea paddling,
Sandcastle making,
Wave watching,
Blustery beaches.

Sand dune climbing,
Rock pool searching,
Starfish catching,
Treasure burying,
Sandy sandwiches.

Boats bobbing,
Beach ball bouncing,
Seagulls squawking,
Sunny weather,
Delightful days,
At the beach.

Rhiannon Williams (9)
St David's Primary School, Moreton-in-Marsh

Sisters

I have a little sister called Neve
She really is a little winner
Even though I wish she was a little thinner

My other sister is called Megan
She really is a pest

Sisters are such a pain
Sisters are so very vain

They can be such fussy eaters
They can also swim metres

But would I swap the two?
I don't know, for who?
No, life would be too dull
Sisters, sisters, sisters.

Phoebe Jarvis (11)
St David's Primary School, Moreton-in-Marsh

November Forest

Deep inside, the shadows of ghostly figures,
Dark trees creak as they solemnly dance with the wind,
Rotten twigs crackle as our heavy feet crunch against them,
It's growing darker in the washed-out light.

We are in the middle of the forest and the carpet
Of golden leaves is like the inside of a pumpkin,
We hear little dewdrops fall like sad tears.

It is dark as we stumble slowly home,
Trees seem to grasp out at us with their bony fingers,
Stones seem to be making faces,
As we trudge across the carpet of leaves the last, weak light fades
And dissolves in the dark, damp dusk.

Elliot Langley (9)
St David's Primary School, Moreton-in-Marsh

The Lion

He prowls around in hot, gleaming sun, stalking his prey,
His muscles ripple, as he pads through dry, brittle grass,
His magnificent mane sways in hot African breeze,
His tail slowly swings flicking badgering flies away,
His big, dark, piercing eyes still focused on his prey,
He pounces, bringing down his victim in one swift, masterful move,
The lion.

Kitty Mounstephen (11)
St David's Primary School, Moreton-in-Marsh

My New Kitten

I bought a brand new kitten,
It's as white as snow,
It's soft and cuddly,
It follows me wherever I go.

Sarah Thompson (9)
St David's Primary School, Moreton-in-Marsh

Please Mrs Andrew

(Based on 'Please Mrs Butler' by Allan Alhberg)

'Please Mrs Andrew
This boy Tommy Andrew
Keeps sticking his smelly sock in my mouth
What shall I do?'
'Sit on the couch, dear,
Take an aeroplane to Jamaica,
My lamb.'

'Please Mrs Andrew,
This boy Tommy Andrew,
Keeps taking my ruler,
What shall I do?'
'Put it in a tin, my dear,
Swallow it if you can,
Do whatever you can, my flower
But don't ask me!'

April Bailey (8)
St Paul's CE Primary School, Gloucester

School

School is so boring
First we do maths
School is so boring
Then we do literacy
School is so boring
After, we have lunch
Yum! Yum! Yum!
Then we do something else
School is so boring
Then we go home
Yes, home time!

Lucy Peck (9)
St Paul's CE Primary School, Gloucester

After The Snow

The ice all bumpy when stood on,
Grit covering the white snow,
Footprints in the crunchy snow,
Lots of water on the table,
Blossom on trees out of place,
Ice looks like glass,
Yellow daffodils starting to grow,
Cold fingers all blue and sore,
The basketball net all frozen,
Steamed-up glasses.

Bradley Meredith (8)
St Paul's CE Primary School, Gloucester

After The Snow

Ice is dripping from the benches and chairs *drip-drop*
Ice is melting really fast
Frozen patterns in crisp packets
Frozen footsteps
Skiddy ice, whoa! Watch out
People playing in snow
Children making snow angels
Children throwing snowballs is such a happy sight.

Conrad Jones (8)
St Paul's CE Primary School, Gloucester

Library

L ibraries have millions of books
I n the library children and adults read
B rainy people like to read
R ia likes reading Harry Potter books
A ll the library people have library cards
R osann likes reading big books
Y ahya likes going to the library.

Solima Ali (8)
St Paul's CE Primary School, Gloucester

It's Friday

It's Friday
It's my day to bring in a toy or book
What shall I bring?
What shall I bring?
I wonder what I could bring?

Shall I bring my Harry Potter book?
No, because Sam will break it
Shall I bring a toy car?
No, because Tom will throw it

I know what I could bring
My toy cars with my racing track.

Georgina Lefeuvre (9)
St Paul's CE Primary School, Gloucester

After The Snow

A frozen bench
A frozen caterpillar
A frozen pipe
A frozen icicle
A frozen hose
A frozen leaf
A frozen pond.

Scott Rickards (9)
St Paul's CE Primary School, Gloucester

House

H ouses can be old
O utside can be very boring
U nsafe house
S awdust everywhere
E normous rooms.

Jonah Windo (9)
St Paul's CE Primary School, Gloucester

After The Snow

You can make footprints in the snow,
You can step in it,
There's soft snow,
There's lots of snow,
Lots of it,
Pattern in solid ice,
It's easy to crack,
You can go ice-skating,
Back indoors it's nice and warm.

Elliot Etherton (8)
St Paul's CE Primary School, Gloucester

Theme Park

T riumph theme park
H ullabaloo, hullabaloo a lot of hullabaloo
E normous theme park
M onstrous roars in the park's walls
E xciting rides that will make you scream

P otato chips and strawberry dips and delicious coconut bars
A mazing magicians will make you wonder
R ocketing roller coasters will make you shout
K ick yourself if you miss it!

Sam Collins (9)
St Paul's CE Primary School, Gloucester

Animals

A nimals are like little angels
N ot like some who try to kill them
I love the way they walk and run,
M y friends like to tickle them, it's so much fun
A ll of them come to eat some food
L ions are always in a grumpy mood
S o if you see a lion run away!

Luke Campbell (9)
St Paul's CE Primary School, Gloucester

Last Day At Secondary School

Last day at secondary school
Last day at secondary school
Children dirty and not as neat as me
Old torn coats hung on wrecked pegs
Old shoes don't shine on people's smelly feet
School hall smells of stinky, smelly, rotten cheese
And smelly eggs
Toilets smell of stinky toilet floors
Children meet horrible teachers
Faces full of dread
Teachers give out old ugly books
Children stare at old dirty pages
Down come the curtains at the ugly stage
It's time to buy a new one.

Yahya Pandor (9)
St Paul's CE Primary School, Gloucester

The Haunted Train

'What are you, nuts?'
'No! Are you?'
'We should go to the train station.'
'We need a ticket please.'
'Here you go.'
'Next train number five.'
'It's haunted, we should go.'
'Help! Help! Help! Help!'
'What are you doing here?'
'This train is haunted.'
'No it's not haunted,
People think that because it's
Scary and dark.'

Daniel Cratchley (8)
St Paul's CE Primary School, Gloucester

Please Mrs Andrews

(Based on 'Please Mrs Butler' by Allan Ahlberg)

'Please Mrs Andrew
This boy Luke
Keeps kicking me, Miss,
What shall I do?'

'Go and kick him back, my dear
Go and take a ride on a horse,
Take your work somewhere else my lamb,
Do whatever you think.'

'Please Mrs Andrew,
This boy Luke,
Keeps calling me names, Miss,
What shall I do?'

'Tell him he is a chicken, my dear,
Pretend he isn't here,
Do what you think best.'

'Please Mrs Andrew,
This boy Luke,
Keeps taking my book, Miss,
What shall I do?'

'Take his book my dear,
Put it in your drawer,
Do whatever you can, my flower,
But don't ask me!'

Keeland Anderson (9)
St Paul's CE Primary School, Gloucester

Snow

Snow is clean and white
Cold as dry ice
Soft as clothes
Freezing like ice cubes
As nice as snow cones.

Cameron Frerker (12)
Siddington CE Primary School

Walking In The Jungle

Walking in the jungle,
Walking in the jungle,
What can I see?
What can I see?
I can see a tiger
Looking at me.

Walking in the jungle,
Walking in the jungle,
What can I see?
What can I see?
I can see an elephant,
But it swung me.

Walking in the jungle,
Walking in the jungle,
What can I see?
What can I see?
I can see a snake,
Long and slithery,
That I've never seen.

Walking in the jungle,
Walking in the jungle,
What can I see?
What can I see?
I can see my mum,
Waving at me!

Emily Kilby (10)
Siddington CE Primary School

Happiness

Happiness is yellow,
It tastes like sugar,
It smells like joy,
It makes you feel good,
It lives in your body.

Emily Cordon (10)
Siddington CE Primary School

The Unicorn

Unicorn galloping hard,
In the shiny sunset,
Across the bed of flowers in the garden,
As her hooves glisten and sparkle.

Unicorn's nose as small as a mouse,
Crystal sparkling blue eyes,
Smelling like flowers,
She never tells lies.

Unicorn in the sky,
Gone past a castle,
She lands on a beach,
Making a sandcastle with lots of shells.

Unicorn took off from the beach,
She flew over mountains and rivers.
Best of all she landed in a forest,
She saw a rabbit, a frog, a badger and even a squirrel.

Unicorn took off again
And don't you know what?
She galloped over a rainbow
And found some gold.

Unicorn had to go back,
It was turning dark
And she would disappear,
She went home.

Daniella Keen (9)
Siddington CE Primary School

Winter

A cold day is like living in cold ice,
An icicle falls from the windy sky,
It's like having loads of ice cubes dropped in your drink
And makes your nose go blue and all ice-cold,
It sounds like rushing wind.

Scarlett Collins (10)
Siddington CE Primary School

Snow

Snow is like dandruff
Sprinkling in the air

Snow is as thick as
Chocolate melting in my mouth

Snow smells fresh
Breathing under my nose

Snow, the taste of ice cream
Dripping to the ground.

Charmaine Linton (10)
Siddington CE Primary School

The Flying Dolphin

You can hear him singing in the background,
Gold wings glistening like glitter.
Gracefully coming out of the water
With a leap and a flap of his wings.
Magic coming out of his blow hole
Then turning to dust,
Anyone who sees him will have a pleasurable feeling inside.

Luke Moore (11)
Siddington CE Primary School

Ice

It feels smooth
It is a glittery-white
It tastes like an ice pop
It smells like sugar
It sounds like wheels spinning on ice.

Aaron Saunders (11)
Siddington CE Primary School

Pegasus

Pegasus, the flying tale,
The hidden male.

His tail flows like mellowing waves,
His eyes are like diamonds and crystals,
His hooves are sparkling gold,
That glides him up to Heaven
And back down to the dazzling Earth.

The only person who rides him has lots of powers,
He's the only one who rides Pegasus.

Charlotte Tickle (9)
Siddington CE Primary School

My Sister Kenning

Fun lover
Cartoon watcher
Liverpool supporter
Morning hater
Bed adorer
My sister!

Letisha Jessop (10)
Siddington CE Primary School

Snow

Snow is white,
It tastes like ice cream,
It smells like ice lollies,
Snow feels like icing sugar,
It sounds like a strong wind blowing.

Ryan Rogers (10)
Siddington CE Primary School

Avalanche

Snow is cold,
It looks like sugar,
Snow is as white as clean paper.
It tastes like ice cream,
But if you ever see an avalanche,
Run for your life!

Keegan Giles (10)
Siddington CE Primary School

The Magnificent Snake

My snake is mottled brown like the forest floor
His thin body is like a twig
His tongue is like a pink fork
His eyes are like little jet beads
He resembles a patch of shadowy floor
I will guard my snake at all times.

Thomas Clare (8)
Temple Guiting School

The Magnificent Dog

My dog is cuddly like a teddy bear,
His face is like a teddy's face,
His nose is like a pool of chocolate,
His eyes are like a waterfall,
He resembles a chocolate bar,
I will guard him with passion.

Rosalind Ball (8)
Temple Guiting School

The Magnificent Dog

My dog is as fast as a black bullet,
Black like the darkest night,
His black shiny fur is like brand new leather,
His obedience is like a trusted friend,
His paws are like a new cuddly teddy,
He resembles a dark shadow in a dark night,
I will love my dog for the rest of my life and longer.

Dido Bolton (8)
Temple Guiting School

The Magnificent Kitten

My kitten is soft like a cotton mitten
Her paw is like a padded soft floor
Her fur is like gentle velvet
Her ears are like little furry triangles
She resembles spotty little plant sitting on a window sill
I will always look after my little kitten
And I will love her forever and ever.

Camilla Mather (9)
Temple Guiting School

The Magnificent Goldfish

My goldfish is golden like gold
His scales are as shiny as the moon
His scales are as shiny as the stars
His spots are as black as coal
He resembles a million pounds
I will guard him with my cat, Snapper.

Max Holland (7)
Temple Guiting School

The Magnificent Dog

My dog is dark
Like the midnight sky,
His bark is like a
Door slamming,
His tail is like
A flag in the wind,
His patches are like
Fresh milk,
He resembles a
Storm cloud,
I will look after him well.

Daniel Feaster (8)
Temple Guiting School

The Magnificent Kitten

My kitten is soft like a fluffy pillow
Her coat is like a warm jumper
Her tail is like a black snake with a white head
Her paws are like a squidgy sponge
She resembles a grey and white patchwork quilt
I will love my sweet little cat forever and ever!

Jemma Moore (9)
Temple Guiting School

The Magnificent Tiger

My tiger is fierce like a horrible bull,
His fur is like a matted towel,
His big belly is like a rugby ball,
His ears are like elephant's ears hanging loose,
He resembles me when I go crazy,
I will keep him forever and never let him go.

Daniel Moore (7)
Temple Guiting School

The Magnificent Horse

My horse is bay
Like bark,
His mane is like
A clump of grass,
His tail is like
A swishing broom,
His hooves are like
Thunder,
He reminds me of Sally
My old horse,
I will guard him with
My life.

William Twiston-Davies (9)
Temple Guiting School

The Magnificent Rabbit

My rabbit is black like the middle of the night
His fur is like a very black small wig
His foot is like a claw foot
His eyes are like special eyes
They are light brown
I will never let him go.

Suzannah Wiggins (8)
Temple Guiting School

The Magnificent Dog

My dog is as black as a furry coat
His eyes are like blue balloons
His ears are like some soft gloves
He resembles a black, cuddly blanket.

Laura Shelley (8)
Temple Guiting School

The Magnificent Dog

My dog is lively
Like the restless wind in winter
Her madness is like a rocket taking off
Her loyalty grows like you and me
Her ears are like soft, cuddly pillows
She resembles a friend playing on long summer days
I will guard her with everything I have, even my life.

Charli-Ann Porter (8)
Temple Guiting School

The Magnificent Dog

My dog is white like powdery snow
And brown like tree bark
His head is like a rounded grapefruit
His tail is like a twisted piece of rope
His eyes are like the blue sea and sky
He resembles an out of control rocket
I will protect him when he's playing.

Luke Tatlow (9)
Temple Guiting School

The Magnificent Dog

My dog is red like flaming fire
Her coat is as thick as whipped cream but even thicker
Her ears are like pig's ears but even bigger
Her teeth are like lion's teeth but even sharper
She resembles a determined squirrel
I will stand by my dog forever
And love her and care for her forever.

Sophia Kelly (8)
Temple Guiting School

The Magnificent Cat

My wonderful cat is lovely and black,
Black like the midnight sky,
Her long, swirly tail is like a snake swirling around,
Her soft black back is like a blanket of velvet,
Her sweet little paws are like bundles of blanket,
She resembles a woollen jumper,
I will always look after my sweet black cat.

Olivia Morrissey (7)
Temple Guiting School

The Magnificent Cat

My beautiful cat is black like the sky at midnight,
Her long swirly tail is like a snake, swirling around,
Her little round tummy is like a white patch of snow,
Her sweet little paws are like a little cot blanket,
She resembles a black quilt,
I will always look after my little black cat.

Sophie Andrews (7)
Temple Guiting School

The Magnificent Dog

My dog, Fluffy, is brown like tree's bark,
His fur is like a tattered blanket,
His floppy ears are like a piece of soft silk,
His fat belly is so, so fat,
He resembles a hoover out of control,
I will guard you, Fluffy, with great care.

Joseph Stirling Lee (8)
Temple Guiting School

The Magnificent Cat

My cat is black,
Like the darkest night,
His eyes are like the gleaming sunshine,
His fur is like a soft, woolly winter hat,
His paws are like two cuddly gloves,
He resembles a pitch-black ball walking through the night,
I will keep my cuddly black cat until he dies.

Alice Wynn (8)
Temple Guiting School

My Magnificent Pony

My pony is as white as snow
Her mane is like a feather duster
Her ears are like pointing pyramids
Her eyes are as blue as the sea
She resembles a Formula One car
I will ride her forever.

Rowland Bowen-Jones (8)
Temple Guiting School

The Magnificent Rabbit

My rabbit is black like the night sky,
His tail is like a sparkling snowflake,
His nose is like a big red bus,
His ears are like a pair of floppy gloves,
He resembles a blanket on a bed,
I will protect my rabbit from the cat.

Christian Forbes (7)
Temple Guiting School

Dinner Time

Silence bringer,
Chop chomper,
Lip licker,
Movement stopper,
Mouth washer,
Gob stopper,
Sip sipper,
Plump maker,
Dinner time . . .

Stephanie Beard (11)
Uplands CP School

Nights

The night puts his black cloak
Over the world,
He sprays his diamonds over
That twist and twirl
And lights the lantern called the moon,
Then he'll go to sleep,
Till the end of the afternoon

Ottilie Baker (9)
Uplands CP School

The Weather In My Head Cinquain

Waking,
Now back at school,
Waiting for my dinner,
I love all my hard work at school,
So cool!

Ruth Townley (10)
Uplands CP School

Seasons

Spring is here . . .
Baby blossoms bloom,
Buds bursting into colour,
Hedgehogs peek outside.

Summer's coming . . .
Golden sun warms hearts,
Bubbly blue waves splash the sand,
Graceful dolphins dive.

Autumn's near . . .
Crimson leaves crunching,
Chilly air begins to nip,
Nature says, 'Goodnight.'

Winter's beginning . . .
Bare trees shivering,
Cottages white with icing
And the white sun drops.

Elizabeth Locke (10)
Uplands CP School

Fire

I can make your oven blaze.
I am showers of colours.
I can awake the dead.
I can turn Guy Fawkes to ash.
I can burn the Devil.
I advise you,
Don't come near.
My blood flows like lava.
I can make you scream with fear,
But you can't live without me.

Samantha Tozer (10)
Uplands CP School

Wind

I can knock down a house
In just a few seconds,
I can cool down your fire
When I creep down your chimney,
I can glide through your garden
And through your flowers,
I can steal into your bedroom
And sneak through your hair.

I can carry the scent of marvellous flowers,
I can carry sand into the air,
I can swap the tops of the greatest trees,
I can rustle the feathers of a bird,
I can snuggle up close to you
When you're asleep.

Cameron Kyte (10)
Uplands CP School

Water

I can put out your fire
And leave you to freeze
I can nourish your crops
With a cool drink
I can give you golden fishes
To swim in your bath
I can wash your hair
And make it sparkle and shine
And never forget
I flow in your bloodstream.

Kelly Bartlett (11)
Uplands CP School

The Boy Who Likes Mash

There was a boy who had a rash
Who liked to eat potato mash

The boy was clever
The boy was tall
The boy was fat
The boy was small

The boy had a great big crash
And after that he found some cash

The cash was green
The cash was cold
The cash was good
The cash was old

The boy fell and made a splash
So after that he jumped in some mash

The mash was cream
The mash was sick
The mash was wide
The mash was thick!

Ryan Thwaite (10)
Uplands CP School

Tiger

Their sharp teeth glisten in the sunlight,
While mouths open for their morning roar,
Then they spot their prey,
Running as they can,
Tails swaying side to side,
They leap, they catch,
Deer is dead,
They tear it apart,
Licking their lips they retreat back home
And fall into a deep, deep sleep.

McCoy Tinsey (10)
Uplands CP School

The Unwanted Mystery Tour

I'm sitting on a broomstick
I think I'm gonna be sick
Witch, where are you taking me?
Flying over southern seas

Will we meet friends in Thailand?
Visit some desert island?
Will we fly to the North Pole?
Up in space, through a black hole?

Take me home, to my warm bed!
Now I wish I hadn't fled!
Witch, where are you taking me?
Won't you listen to my plea?

Roseanna Dressel (10)
Uplands CP School

Thank You Letter

Dear Aunt Nora,
Thanks for the brill Barbie watch
It was fantastic,
Really, it was!
I always used it
But
Yesterday a sad thing happened,
I accidentally dropped it,
Down the toilet,
That's why I can't show you
How much I love it,
Love Jamie.

Jamie Mather (11)
Uplands CP School

Under The Sea

If I lived under the sea,
I'd eat lobsters for my tea,
I'd ride the gentle waves
And play in fantastic caves.
I'd steal the oyster's lovely pearls
And hide from watery whirls,
But I'd rather just be like me
And not live life under the sea!

Hannah Cullis (10)
Uplands CP School

Wind

I can sit on a hedgehog without getting tattooed
I can rock a wind chime with my ghostly hands
I can blow a house down with a flick of my finger
I can rot down wood with my breath
I can go through a house without being seen
I can make you cold without being there
I can make furious fire
I can make the sea have giant, furious waves
Can you guess what I am?

Liam Deane (10)
Uplands CP School

A Road

Frog flattener
Hedgehog killer
Knee cutter
Hard killer
Wheel popper
Transport carrier
Town crosser.

Thomas Legge (9)
Uplands CP School

Wind

I can smash a car off the road
I can chop a dam in half and not hurt my hand
I can spin bees around into your hair
I can rip trees in half and throw them for miles
I can carry a flower over the ocean
I can knock a chimney off the roof
I can creep through your house and watch TV
I can pick you up by your feet
And go anywhere, go where I want.

Tim Parnell (9)
Uplands CP School

Have You Seen?

Have you seen the rain that can flood a lake like a tap?
Have you seen the snow that can bury a school like sand?
Have you seen the hail that can crush monster trucks like boulders?
Have you seen the lightning that can power a factory like a battery?
Have you seen the tornadoes that can lift a skyscraper like
a pro wrestler?
Have you seen the earthquakes that swallow a city like a whale?
I have.

Peter Costello (11)
Uplands CP School

Have You Ever Had An Itch In Your Ear?

Have you ever had an itch in your ear?
I only get it in a leap year
It can anger you and put you up one more gear
It's even worse than having an ant up your rear!
I find it ever so, ever so, ever so queer
Have you ever had an itch in your ear?

Daniel Omnes (10)
Uplands CP School

Inside Me

Some people think I hate my brother,
But on the inside I love my brother,
People think I'm not scared of anything,
But I am,
I'm scared of heights and other things,
Most people think my best sport is football,
But it's not,
Mine is baseball or basketball,
People don't think I'm scared of bugs
And all other insects,
Some people think I never lie,
But I do!

Daniel Button (10)
Uplands CP School

Inside Me

Inside myself I am not shy but loud,
Wanting to be the leader of the group.
I may not be loud on the outside,
But I'm loud inside.
Inside me I am warm,
Beginning to grow.
I feel I'm the best inside,
But on the outside I know other people are better,
Outside I feel I have to go back,
To correct all the wrong things I've done,
But not on the inside!

Holly Clay (10)
Uplands CP School

Letter Poem

Dear Auntie Angela,
The pink nightgown
You sent was great,
You really didn't need to go to all that trouble,
I can't get it over my head,
But I don't mind that a bit,
I will use it as a hat instead!
Nobody buys me presents like you do,
That's why I always like my presents from you.

Jade Riches (9)
Uplands CP School

Nasty Nature

Nasty nature slithering around your toes
Nasty nature crawling up your nose
Nasty nature nesting in your hair
Nasty nature sometimes as big as a bear
Nasty nature wondering what's in here
Nasty nature burrowing in your ear
Nasty nature beware because they're everywhere.

Bradley Gardiner
Uplands CP School

Snowballs

Snowballs flying through the air,
Kids throwing them without a care!
They plunge down and hit the ground,
Then they will be left to melt, unfound!
Kids roll them up into balls,
Then one kid stands up and calls . . .
'Snowballs!'

Holly Hart (10)
Woodmancote Primary School

The Day It Snowed!

The sky was dull
And everyone was gloomy
When all of a sudden
It appeared . . .

The snow had come
Like never before
Falling from the sky
Like a shot from a gun

The ground was covered in seconds
It looked like a carpet of snowdrops
Thick and fast, it continued to fall
Everyone looked surprised

It stopped as quick as it started
Everywhere was covered in snow
Everyone was excited
That was the day is snowed.

Stephen Dolman (9)
Woodmancote Primary School

The Candle Poem

The matches rumble, a tree has collapsed without a prayer.
A flaming eagle has risen from its home and lights up the
room with anger.
The flame has erupted; the sun has risen in the darkness because of
the lion's call.
Time has stood still; the flame is like an erupting volcano
frozen in impact.
The flame is moving again; the hand walks through the flaming door
like a knight slaying a dragon.
The flame has stood still once more; it's like a rosebud in winter with
snow biting the petals.

Michael Robey (9)
Woodmancote Primary School

My Sister

I have an older sister,
On her toe she has a blister.

Her room is never clean,
To me she is always mean.

She gets up at the crack of dawn,
If you see her jeans they are always torn.

She can be frightfully rude
And never in a good mood.

She never has a wash,
You couldn't call her posh.

Sometimes I need a new sister,
But when she isn't here, I miss her.

Georgina Burrows (10)
Woodmancote Primary School

I'm Scared

I'm scared of the miles and miles of spooky, dark sky.
I'm scared as the wolves roam around.
The darkness staring back in my face as the stars glisten above.
Night-time is what I don't like with the stars as my only comfort.
In the sky at the strike of midnight; silence.
Ghosts make the floor creak in the haunted house next door.
Howl, the wolves have come again in the dead of night.
The midnight sky is dark, dark for miles and miles; I'm scared.
I shiver at the thought of it, the thought of the owl's big bright eyes;
The eyes that glare,
The eyes that stare.
I'm scared!

Louisa Ripley (9)
Woodmancote Primary School

My Rabbit

My rabbit is called Toffee,
his coat is the colour of milky coffee.
He eats lots of flowers,
he thinks they have magic powers!

My rabbit he loves to play,
he does it every day.
Toffee jumps up and down,
he thinks it's fun, never a frown.

Eleanor Walsh (9)
Woodmancote Primary School

Snowmen

S nowmen are good, snowmen are bad!
N o one knows what snowmen do when you're fast asleep.
O n the ground snowmen are happy.
W hen the hot sun shines down, the snowmen disappear.
M um and Dad call me in for tea.
E veryone is going to bed.
N ow the story has to end, goodnight!

Emily Mackenzie (9)
Woodmancote Primary School

Midnight

A little girl who roams the streets,
At the dead of night, when it snow and sleets
The streetlamps shine upon her shadow,
But all you can see is the dark and spooky meadow,
This girl is unique, she has special powers,
Her name is Midnight and that's all that matters.

Laura Winstanley (10)
Woodmancote Primary School

Our Fate

I hope I am in bed
Because a small black dot is going into my head
It oddly felt like a stud
But then I realised it was just of mud
I was lucky even though it wasn't a dream
I just found out we're going over the whole team
And we were going over as bait
And they knew like me this would be our fate.

Felix Torrance (9)
Woodmancote Primary School

People

People large and people small,
People mean and people strenuous.
People fat and people thin,
People lively and people that win.
All the different people that live in our world
Have one thing in common,
We all live in the same place!

Jasmin Weaver (9)
Woodmancote Primary School

Butterfly

Butterfly flying up in the sky
Butterfly flying very, very high
Butterfly green, butterfly blue
Butterfly orange, butterfly red
Butterfly beautiful, now and forever.

Hannah Andrews (7)
Woodmancote Primary School

Ten White Snowmen!

Ten white snowmen playing in a line,
One got knocked out and then there were nine.!

Nine white snowmen fishing with bait,
One fell in and then there were eight!

Eight white snowmen admiring Heaven,
One jumped up and then there were seven!

Seven white snowmen playing with sticks,
One got poked and then there were six!

Six white snowmen looking at a hive,
One got stung and then there were five!

Five white snowmen knocking at a door,
One fell over and then there were four!

Four white snowmen looking at me,
One melted and then there were three!

Three white snowmen eating a stew,
One fell dead and then there were two!

Two white snowmen chewing a bun,
One walked home and then there was one!

One white snowman thinking he's a hero,
He was knocked over and then there were zero!

Alexis Munro (10)
Woodmancote Primary School

Ten Little Dogs

Ten little dogs were drinking wine,
One got drunk then there were nine.

Nine little dogs were always late,
One wasn't, then there were eight.

Eight little dogs went up to Heaven,
One turned into an angel then there were seven.

Seven little dogs were in a hive,
One got stung then there were five.

Five little dogs were sweeping the floor,
One fell over then there were four.

Four little dogs trying to catch a bee,
One had stings all over then there were three.

Three little dogs all drinking from the loo,
One fell down then there were two.

Two little dogs were having fun,
One didn't then there was one.

One little dog eating a bun,
He walked away then there were none.

Evie Torrance (7)
Woodmancote Primary School

The Seasons

Summer

Summer is very hot, very hot,
Unlike winter that's not,
The sun shines bright,
Like a yellow light,
You always have fun,
When you're outside in the sun.

Autumn

Animals go into hibernation.
There's some precipitation,
Squirrels hide their nuts in the ground,
Sleeping animals don't make a sound,
The leaves turn brown,
Before they fall down.

Winter

The big brown trees,
Begin to freeze,
In winter you get snow,
But the rivers don't flow,
Snow falls to the ground,
But it doesn't make a sound.

Spring

Forests grow back to their lush rich green,
Wildlife now can be seen,
Baby lambs run and play,
They have fun every day,
Pretty flowers grow,
But the wind will still blow.

Joshua Phillips (10)
Woodmancote Primary School

Ten Pink Bunnies

Ten pink bunnies singing a rhyme
One lost the words then there were nine
Nine pink bunnies hanging on a gate
One got off then there were eight
Eight pink bunnies going to Devon
One broke down then there were seven
Seven pink bunnies eating Weetabix
One was sick then there were six
Six pink bunnies in a beehive
One got stung then there were five
Five pink bunnies skidding in the hall
One hurt their knee then there were four
Four pink bunnies in a big tree
One fell out then there were three
Three pink bunnies looking for a clue
One found it then there were two
Two pink bunnies eating a hot bun
One got burnt then there was one
One pink bunny looking at the sun
He got hot then there were none.

Georgia Lines (6)
Woodmancote Primary School

Ponies

A flowing tail,
A flying mane,
Hooves galloping along the fields,
The horse that is in my dreams I'm about to meet.

His name is Ben,
He's gentle and kind,
I wish Mum could see him,
But before I ride him, my legs need to grow.

Emma Jenkins (7)
Woodmancote Primary School

Ten Little Rabbits

Ten little rabbits singing a rhyme
One sang out of tune, then there were nine
Nine little rabbits eating birthday cake
One ate a candle, then there were eight
Eight little rabbits hopping up to Devon
One fell over, then there were seven
Seven little rabbits eating Weetabix
One went mad then there were six
Six little rabbits learning to drive
One didn't put the handbrake on then there were five
Five little rabbits breaking the law
One went to prison, then there were four
Four little rabbits climbing up a tree
One fell down, then there were three
Three little rabbits playing with their shoes
One got tied up in knots, then there were two
Two little rabbits eating a bun
One didn't like it and then there was one
One little rabbit having lots of fun
Then he felt lonely and went to find his mum!

Philippa Rawlinson (7)
Woodmancote Primary School

Winter Poem

W hite snow covers all the land
 I cicles melt in the warm sun
N ice snowball fights
T ight clothes, warm scarves
E njoy yourself playing in the snow
R eindeer standing on the rooftop.

Ellie Knight (7)
Woodmancote Primary School

The Break Of Dawn

A peek of light appears amongst the mountains,
Their highest points covered in snow.
Ascending slowly the sun rises higher pushing the darkness
Away as a freshly awoken man draws back his curtains
To greet a beautiful new day.
Softly, a wonderful chirping sound begins,
As musical to the ears as a flute playing a magnificent piece.
Drifting through the tranquil air, a blissful scent of ruby-red roses
And amazing wild flowers wafts amongst fields of
                                    luscious green grass.
The dazzling sunrise of jewels of all colours reveals
The scenery of emerald forests filled with exotic wildlife.
A new day has begun.

Amy Finch (9)
Woodmancote Primary School

Elephants

Elephants big and elephants small,
elephants short and elephants tall.

Elephants wet, elephants dry,
elephants pointing trunks to the sky.

Elephants' tusks grey and white,
elephants trumpeting day and night.

Elephants nice, elephants not,
elephants running on the spot.

Elephants sleepy and asleep,
elephants' alarms going *beep, beep, beep!*

Jessica Butler (7)
Woodmancote Primary School

My Hamster

Sawdust nibbler
Fast runner
Quick nibbler
Slow eater
Holds food
House maker
Day sleeper
Night waker.

Charlie Hitchcock (8)
Wycliffe Preparatory School

Super Diver

Good swimmer
Acceptable legs
Strong back
Deep swimmer
Incredible gobbler
Crazy dancer
Slow walker
Super diver!

Kerianne Genders (7)
Wycliffe Preparatory School

The Round Table

Funny table
Wooden object
Camelot castle
Bravery table
Distressed meetings
Sit down
Battle people.

Victoria Dickinson (7)
Wycliffe Preparatory School

My Brother

TV nicker
Banana eater
Face flicker
Pre-prep goer

Table worker
Cupboard looker
Pencil sharpener
Big reader

It's my brother!

Kieran Powell (8)
Wycliffe Preparatory School

Badger

Nocturnal eyes
Underground home
Excellent climber
Small creature
Superb sniffer
Soft fur
Razor claws
Quiet stepper
Very scared
Digs nicely
Bad and brave.

Oliver Cawthorne (7)
Wycliffe Preparatory School

Dolphin Haiku

It jumps through the waves,
Soars over the sharks and crabs,
Over old shipwrecks.

Imogen Bell (7)
Wycliffe Preparatory School

Dog

Furry friend
Great love
Excitingly great
Jumping side
Great thing
Flea bag
Bird catching
Very rude
Nicely bad
Very sad
Eye catching
Greatly matching.

Charlotte Macpherson-Spence (8)
Wycliffe Preparatory School

Penguin

Ice glider
Slippery slider

Fishy eater
Water drinker

Slippery ice
Freezing ice.

Fiona Kennedy (8)
Wycliffe Preparatory School

Who Is It?

Buzz, buzz, buzz, bees buzz
Sting-a-sting-a-sting dead!
Buzzzzzz! Guess who it is?

Harry Hemming (7)
Wycliffe Preparatory School

Spring

Sun shimmer
Bird building
Daffodil flowering
Blue sky
Snow hider
Leaf cruncher
Scamper squirrels
Children chases
Low showers.

Saffron Teagle-Brown (7)
Wycliffe Preparatory School

David Beckham

Famous player
Goal taker
In Spain
First place
Both footer
Midfield player
Rich person.

Lewis McKissick (8)
Wycliffe Preparatory School

Super Machine

Big wheels
Back blinds
Seven seater
Turning machine
Nice alloys
Leather seater.

Patrick Price (8)
Wycliffe Preparatory School

Guess What?

Jungle lover
Nature mother
Tree swinger
Trouble bringer
Cheeky animal
Banana cannibal
Ticklish arms
In palms . . .
Fergus' favourite!

Fergus Menendez (8)
Wycliffe Preparatory School

My Dog

Loud barker
Frog eater
Cat watcher
Grass eater
Mud scratcher
Bone stealer
Always good.

Lucy Moule (8)
Wycliffe Preparatory School

My Dog

Tail wagger,
Bone cruncher,
Food lover,
Paw shaker,
Walk admirer,
Ball chaser.

Jemma Buck (7)
Wycliffe Preparatory School

The Wolf Ways

Night seeker
Meat eater
Quiet hunter
Loud howler
Fast runner
Pack traveller
Silent paws
Quick hearing
Long legs
Bushy tail.

Rachel Connolly (8)
Wycliffe Preparatory School

Sleeping Cat

Paw licker
Mice chaser
Milk drinker
Food eater
Deep sleeper
Purring loudly
Tree climber
Wall chaser.

Jasmine Bailey (8)
Wycliffe Preparatory School

England Player

Mad kicker
Good striker
Great kicker
Fast runner
England player.

Henry Scott (7)
Wycliffe Preparatory School

Cats

Dog hater
Mice chaser
Bird catcher
Milk snatcher
All furry
All purry
Grass licker
Dog fighter
Mouse eater
Mouse cheater
One black cat.

Aimee Wilkinson (7)
Wycliffe Preparatory School

Lizard

Bug smacker
Stealth walker

Quick snacker
Terrain lover

Tongue flicker
Bug finder

Forest dweller
Luck bringer.

Ralph Williams (8)
Wycliffe Preparatory School

A Cold Night Haiku

A wind-blowing night
Wind whistling through the bare trees
A cold, windy night.

Benjamin Capehorn (7)
Wycliffe Preparatory School

The Kangaroo

High jumper
Feet thumper
Pouch keeper
Baby sneaker
Good leaper
Brilliant sleeper
Warm placer
Jumping racer
Smooth fur
Never purr
Food stealer
No healer.

Ruth Vickers (8)
Wycliffe Preparatory School

Fairies

Tiny people
Little wings
Magic wand
Incredibly kind
Likes hiding
Tiny voices
Sprinkles dust
Flying sorcerers
Disguised people
Flower lovers
Sun likers
Pixie chasers
Rainbow lovers.

Camila Poccard (8)
Wycliffe Preparatory School